QUANTUM PHYSICS

BASIC PRINCIPLES

DISCOVER THE MOST MIND BLOWING THEORIES THAT GOVERN THE UNIVERSE AND THE WORLD AROUND US

LOEW T. KAUFMANN

TABLE OF CONTENT

There are no scenarios in which the publisher or the original author of this work can be in any fashion deemed liable for any hardship or damages that may befall them after undertaking information described herein.

Additionally, the information in the following pages is intended only for informational purposes and should thus be thought of as universal.

As befitting its nature, it is presented without assurance regarding its prolonged validity or interim quality.

Trademarks that are mentioned are done without written consent and can in no way be considered an endorsement from the trademark holder.

INTRODUCTION

Without a doubt, Einstein's work reshaped the world in so many ways that it would take an entire library to explain them in plain English only. In the scientific community (and, dare we say, outside of it too), Einstein is seen as a sort of demi-god - an irrefutable authority that nobody dares to touch.

Nobody except quantum physicists, that is.

If Einstein's theory of relativity is so well-regarded and accepted, why do we even bother with quantum mechanics, then? What demon sets so many contemporary scientific researchers on the path of actually trying to reconcile the worlds of classical physics and quantum physics?

Well, the one reason quantum mechanics is accepted and still very much a topic of discussion is that it would manage to solve what classical physics couldn't. And, it would work to push the boundaries of knowledge and technology beyond the edges of the imaginary. Into a spectrum, we only dared to touch with our thoughts until not very long ago.

September 7, 2014, might have seemed like any other day of fall in the Northern Hemisphere. The leaves were probably slightly yellow by then, and the heat of the summer was slowly starting to wear out. Maybe it even rained a little in the morning, and by the time cities were waking up to life, the fog of a slightly chillier night vanished, leaving room for a perfect day of autumn.

What everyone must know is that September 7, 2014, was the day the Theory of Everything officially saw the light of day. You might have learned about it because there was a movie on the life of Stephen Hawking. Or you might have even stumbled upon it long before the movie came out.

What is essential, however, is that the Theory of Everything is one of the most significant attempts at unifying both the theory of relativity and the quantum theory. What was started in the 1920s by Albert Einstein was finally beginning to make sense eight decades under the hands of Stephen Hawking?

The Theory of Everything is, perhaps, one of the most ambitious projects ever. It is one of the theories that is bound to change every single little thing - not just in physics, but in science as a whole, and, soon enough, in humanity's perception of pretty much every area of their lives.

What the Theory of Everything tries to do is finally build a bridge between quantum mechanics and the theory of relativity. Some would even provoke to say that it will "tell the mind of God" (Marshall, 2010) and that it will hold the key to humanity answering the questions it has been trying to answer for a very, very long time now.

There are several candidates for the Theory of Everything. Some of them are implausible to be proven in the equation or practice, but some of them stand out as sane options that might be the final answer to everything.

Out of these, we would like to take the time to name the two most important contenders. We consider it is essential for you to know what the most crucial work in physics is doing now - and as such, we will take the time to expand, just a little bit, on these two theories.

One of them is called "String Theory," and what it says is that there is a ten-dimensional space we are living in. That sounds more than mind- boggling, we know, but wait until you hear more of it.

According to the String Theory, the point-like bits of speck physics are one-dimensional objects (called "strings"). The theory pronounces that these strings circulate through space and that they interconnect with each other. When viewed at from distant, a line beholds like any other common particle (with a mass, charge, etc. that are indomitable by the vibrational state of the string). For example, one of the vibrational states of the line is signified by gravitation (a particle that relays the gravitational force, that is).

In essence, the Theory of Everything relies on quantum gravity, and it aims to address a wide range of questions in fundamental physics - such as what is going on with black holes, how the universe was formed, how to improve nuclear physics, and how to handle condensed matter physics better.
Ideally, string theory will unify gravity and particle physics (which is one of the main points that have to be bridged between classical physics and quantum mechanics). At the moment, however, it is not evident how much of this theory can be adapted to the real world and how much of it will allow for changes in its details.
The other theory competing with string theory for the title of "The Theory of Everything" is the Loop Quantum Gravity Theory. This paradigm is heavily based on Einstein's work, and it was elaborated towards the middle of the 1980s. To understand it, you need to remember the fact that, according to Einstein, gravity is not a force per se, but a property of space-time.
Up until the Loop Quantum Gravity Theory, there have been several attempts to prove that gravity can be treated as a quantum force, like electromagnetism or nuclear energy, for example. However, these attempts have failed.
What the Loop Quantum Gravity concept tries to fix is to ground the crossing amongst conventional physics and quantum physics on Einstein's geometric formulation. Preferably, this will verify that the universe and period are quantized the same approach as energy and momentum are in the quantum process.

If physicists manage to prove the Loop Quantum Gravity Theory, space-time will be pictured with space and time being granular, which would consequently mean that a minimum space exists. In other words, concurring to the Loop Quantum Gravity Theory, space is made out of a fine fabric of woven finite loops called "spin networks."

Although String Theory seems to be a lot more popular in mainstream media (mainly because some of its proponents are quite popular themselves, even well outside of scientific circles - like Michio Kaku, for example), the Loop Quantum Gravity Theory should not be dismissed in any way. Most of its implications are related to the birth of the universe, the reason for which it is also called the Big Bang Theory - and, perhaps, the reason for which the eponymous tv show was called that way as well.

In addition to the string and loop quantum gravity theories, you might also stumble upon several other candidates to become the Theory of Everything. Some of them include the Causal Dynamical Triangulations Theory, the Quantum Einstein Gravity Theory, the Quantum Gravity Theory, or the Internal Relativity Theory.

All of these theories show that active efforts are being put into unifying quantum theory and the more classical physics, proving that the vast majority of the science community pays quite a lot of attention to quantum mechanics.

Who are we to dismiss them, then? Just because things are still foggy, it doesn't mean that they will stay this way forever. And the whole essence of science, in general, is to dream and aim for something bigger, more comprehensive, and more efficient. It has always been this way, and it will always be.

And when it comes to the ultimate dream, nothing gets as close to the grandeur, the supersite, and the brevity of the quantum mechanics world - precisely because it is the only theory that will finally give us a well-deserved push forward into a wide range of discoveries.

What Should You Believe?

It is up to you. We request you to learn more about both quantum and classical physics and to make up your mind. The beauty of physics and research in this field is that nothing is ever fixed and that theories that might have seemed unbreakable have been consistently broken throughout history - starting with, for example, the flatness of the Earth.
Believe what you think is true based on your readings and research, but stay true to the fallible nature of everything!

BEFORE QUANTUM PHYSICS:

The size of an electron is to a dust speck as the dust speck is to the entire earth" _ Robert Jastrow

James Clerk Maxwell, a great man who brought two halves that seemed irreconcilable to a whole in the 1860s.
His great efforts married electricity with magnetism and revolutionized our understanding of light.
So, we will briefly explore the connections between light, color, and heat. We will encounter a curious physics mystery of the 19th-century and the first step to fall on the road from classical to quantum physics.

NEWTON'S LIGHT CORPUSCLES

Have you ever imagined of becoming a celebrity in your job or sport? Have you ever thought you could become a champion in both roles?
Sir Isaac Newton was a myth in 2 fields. Not only he invented the laws of motion, but he also laid the foundations for geometric optics.
Newton believed that light was made up of tiny particles that travel in straight lines called rays. These small corpuscles bounce off the mirrors, and when they meet a lens, they always bend slightly at the entrance and exit but travel in straight lines along the way.

An alternative theory of light emerged. Rather than small particles traveling in straight lines through space, this new theory claimed that light was made up of small vibrations in some underlying medium, like water waves traveling from the wake of a boat to the shore.
Newton did not accept this wave concept because it seemed inconsistent with his geometric approach of lenses and mirrors.
Given Newton's high reputation among physicists, his rejection of the wave of light theory did not emerge for many decades. Nevertheless, even Newton failed to pass the experimental tests, and in the end - two centuries - his classical theory of light particles had been definitively discarded.

YOUNG'S DOUBLE-SLIT EXPERIMENT

Now let us go back and explore the theory of the wave of light in detail. First of all, we need to establish some bases on wave phenomena.
Imagine sitting on a fishing boat on a calm, windless morning. Suddenly a motorboat is speeding past you. You should now notice that your boat starts floating up and down. This happens because the past speedboat sends a wave across the water.

Now, imagine that another motorboat is going on the opposite side at about the same time. You will then notice that when the crests of the two waves arrive simultaneously, your boat floats twice as much. This phenomenon is known as constructive interference.
On the other hand, when one crest of one boat's waves coincides with a depression of the others, your boat does not move at all. This is called destructive interference.

For all other cases, your boat's height will be roughly in the middle, as calculated by adding the heights of the two individual waves.
This method of arithmetic addition of wave heights is known to physicists as overlap. More generally, the interaction between multiple waves is called wave interference. Moreover, it is an unexpected observation of this effect that has finally allowed the wave theory of light to emerge from Newton's shadow.

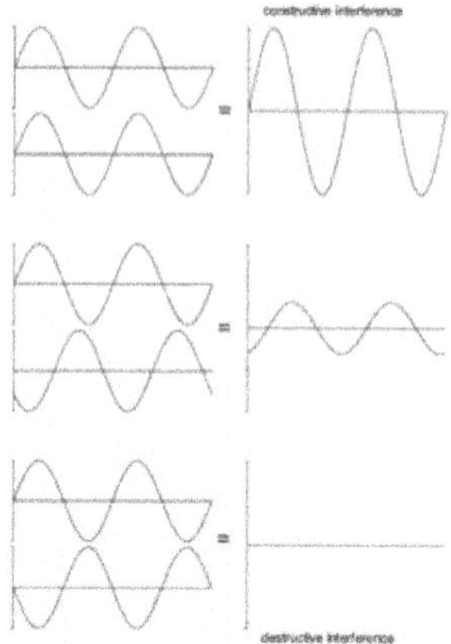

What does this have to complete with light?
Well, imagine now that you are in a bedroom with no light. Open the door of an illuminated corridor. You would expect a large rectangular shape to light upon the bedroom wall as light passes between the door and its frame.
Nevertheless, what would happen if I closed the door more so that the space between the door and the frame became thin? At the beginning of the 19th century, one of Newton's compatriots, Thomas Young, tried to answer.

He cut a small pair of slits into an otherwise opaque object and placed it in a dark room. He pointed a beam of light through the slits, then looked at what appeared on a screen a few meters away. Instead of seeing two thin stripes appear, a theory predicted by Newton (geometric optics), he noticed a series of stripes aligned along with the screen like a fence. The explanation for this observation conflicted with light particles' theory: light was behaving like a wave. Young speculated that the initial ray was a wave that crossed the room. When interacting with the two slits (points A and B in its original shape), each slit served as the source of a new wave, just like the circular pattern formed when water waves pass through a narrow channel. As they move away from the cracks, the two waves begin to overlap and interfere. When looking at the darkened screen, the resulting pattern is a series of stripes: dark when a crest of one wave meets a depression of the other (points C, D, E, and F) and light in which the crests of the two waves coincide.

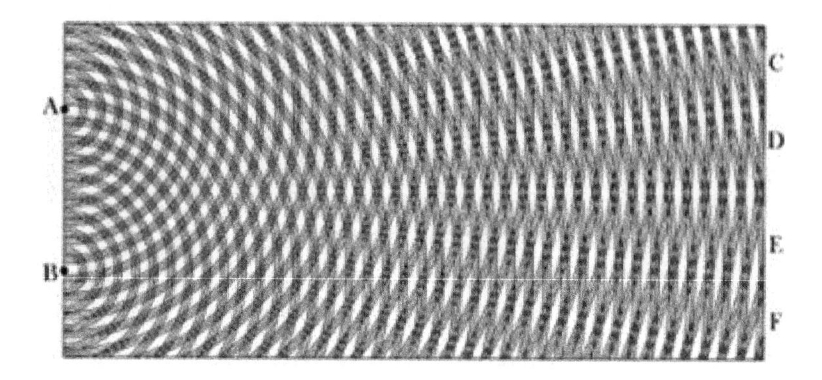

The image Dr. Young saw on his screen is a diffraction pattern.

Diffraction patterns can be observed whenever two waves interfere with each other, be they water waves or light passing through a narrow slit in a dark room. Although initially treated with skepticism, Young's work gradually gained general approval.
Before long, he had managed to reverse Newton's particle theory on the light.
The final blow was placed about half a century by Scottish physicist James Clerk Maxwell.

THE FAMOUS MAXWELL EQUATIONS

In the Maxwell era, physicists had already understood that static electricity is created whenever they rub, for example, a piece of amber with a rabbit fur. They had also noticed that a compass needle moves every time a magnet is placed nearby. Given the very different nature of these effects, these two phenomena were considered independent and unrelated.

However, at about the same time, some critical observations made it clear that electricity and magnetism can be connected. Maxwell derived a series of four simple equations, which showed that electricity and magnetism were only two sides of the same coin. The two phenomena have always been connected by something called an electromagnetic field.

Just as one gravitational field allows any mass to drag on another, Maxwell's electromagnetic field allows any positive charge to repel positive charges and attract negative charges.

Maxwell showed that a flow of moving electrical charges produces an electromagnetic field that could move a compass needle. He proceeded on to say that if those moving charges were to increase in speed or change direction, they would produce an electromagnetic wave that would travel in space.

This wave is a disturbance in the electromagnetic field itself.

Maxwell's classical electrodynamics was very powerful. He explained almost every electrical or magnetic phenomenon known at the time.

For example, it could successfully explain why colors emerged from Newton's prism and why Young's double slits formed a diffraction pattern.
Physicists and engineers still use it today to define many electrical and magnetic phenomena with extreme correctness.
It could also be used to calculate the rate at which electromagnetic waves should travel through space.
Maxwell claimed that these waves move at the same speed that physicists had been considered for light rays.
When Maxwell's theory was confirmed several decades, there was little doubt that light was indeed a wave phenomenon.

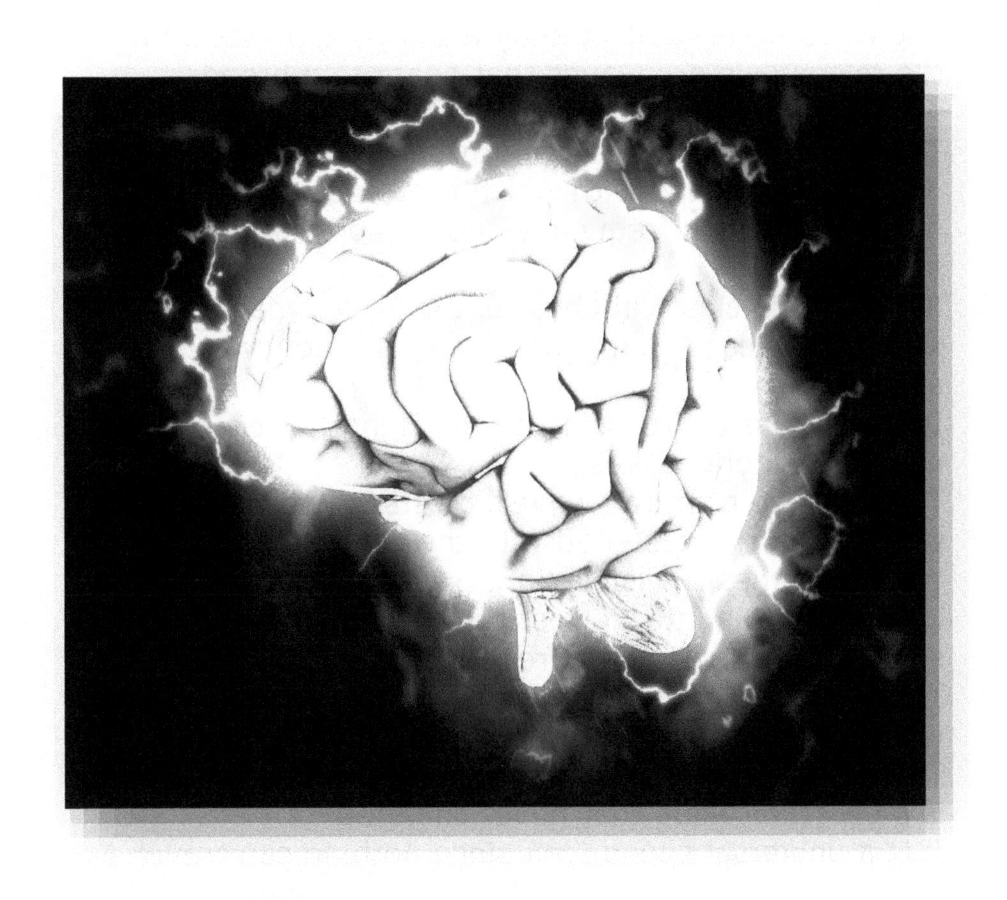

ELECTROMAGNETIC SPECTRA

Today we know that visible light is not the only type of electromagnetic wave out there.
The radio waves collected by the mobile phone and the microwave are waves that adapt to a broad electromagnetic spectrum.
The only difference between these different types of waves is the speed with which they oscillate: this quantity is called frequency and is represented by the symbol f.
According to classical physics, the electromagnetic spectrum is continuous, and every frequency is allowed.
It is also feasible to measure the "length" of electromagnetic waves.
The distance from the wave's crests is known as the wavelength (represented with the Greek symbol λ).
When it comes to visible light, red light has the longest wavelength (lowest frequency), while the shortest purple (highest frequency).
The last quantity needed to describe electromagnetic waves is the speed with which they travel.
The swiftness of light is denoted by the symbol c. This is a constant value that never changes.
It is a universal speed limit since nothing can travel faster than c. Mathematically, the three quantities are connected by the equation $c = \lambda f$.
Since all electromagnetic waves travel at the same speed, longer wavelengths have lower frequencies, and shorter wavelengths have higher ones.
Most light sources, like the sun, actually emit light that spans a range of frequencies.

Physicists also use particular light sources that emit pure light of a single frequency or monochromatic light.
Compared to the human-sized water waves that we observed earlier when we were on the boat, the light waves are much shorter.
The wavelength of the orange light emitted by a lamppost is approximately 60 millionths of a centimeter (0.00006 cm).
It is this "smallness" of the light waves that made Newton curious.
Light waves are very short compared to the size of our mirror, for example.
This means that when the light bounces or passes through it, the deviation from the movement in a straight line is imperceptible.
Therefore, Newton's geometric optics work well for almost all everyday applications.
It no longer works only when light interacts with microscopic objects, such as Young's thin double slits.
If we travel along the electromagnetic spectrum towards gradually longer wavelengths, we will arrive at infrared radiation.
Infrared radiation is not visible to the naked eye, but tools such as night vision goggles can easily detect it.
They work by sensing the thermal radiation (heat) emitted by the objects they see.
We stressed that Maxwell's classical electrodynamics could explain almost all the electromagnetic phenomena that we observe every day.
Spectra emitted by heated solids and excited gases, however, are exceptions.

Although he will be remembered forever as the father

of electromagnetism, one of Maxwell's most famous theories had nothing to do with this topic.
In 1873, he turned to the British Association for the Advancement of Science to discuss "molecules." However, he referred more generally to the concept that gases are composed of small particles that move intensely.

He claimed that the air in the classroom was full of molecules traveling in all directions at speeds of around 17 miles per minute. Maxwell and his contemporaries understood that the air temperature and pressure around them were directly proportional to the speed of gas particles.
There are approximately 1x1023 particles in the volume of a beach ball. Since the velocity of these will vary somewhat over a specific range, it is more accurate to say that the ambient temperature and pressure are determined by the average velocity of all those particles.
The general relationship between particle velocity, temperature, and pressure is termed thermodynamics. It can be classified as the third and final pillar of classical physics.
As highlighted by Maxwell's important lesson, its center is the small particles that make up the air.

FUNDAMENTAL PRINCIPLES AND LAWS

As every excellent reading on electromagnetism will tell you, a single slit, or a pinhole, will produce an interference pattern.

However, a less pronounced one than a larger slit provides. It is a natural experiment that you can do by yourself—just take a piece of paper, poke a little round hole with a pin or needle, and look towards a light source. You will observe the image of the light source surrounded by several concentric colored fringes (the colors appear only because, fortunately, the world we live in is not monochromatic).

In this case, you see that, even though we are dealing with only one slit, some weak but still clearly visible secondary minima and maxima fringes can be observing.

An important point to keep in mind is to avoid a common misconception (which is frequently promulgate in some popular science readings), which states that only two or more slits can produce interference fringes, whereas, for the single slit, interference effects disappear. It is not entirely correct.

True, it is easier to produce more pronounced interference patterns with more than one slit (or pinhole). For most applications, especially when the wavelength of the incident wave is much smaller than the size of the aperture, these effects can be neglected.

However, strictly speaking, a single slit also produces small diffraction and interference phenomena.

An elegant explanation of how interference comes into being, also for a single slit, dates back to the French physicist A. J. Fresnel. He borrowed an idea from Huygens (hence the name 'Huygens Fresnel principle'), according to which every single point on a wavefront should itself be considered a point-source of a spherical wave.
Along the slit's aperture emit at the same time their spherical wavefronts, which, however, when seen from a position on the screen, add up to produce an interference pattern. The reason for this is not so difficult to visualize.
Since all fronts are initiate in different locations along with the aperture, they will also travel a different path length, which implies that they have various phase shifts when they overlap on the screen.
For instance, where we saw the two paths of the two sources from the edges. Fresnel was able to show that if one sums up all of the spherical wavefronts coming from the points of the opening of the single slit and projects these onto all the points along with the detector screen, then one obtains the known diffraction and interference patterns indeed.

THE HUYGENS-FRESNEL PRINCIPLE

If we recap the same experiment with a slit that has a size close to the wavelength of our incoming wavefront, then we see that the interference fringes disappear.
Only when the size of the slit is equal to or smaller than the wavelength are the fringes absent. It is because the slit is so low that only a single point-source can form a spherical wavefront with a wavelength equal to the slit size, and there can be no path difference and phase shift with some other source which could produce the interference pattern. However, diffraction has become very large instead, so that the photons will displace themselves on a relatively large area on the detector screen, according to a bell-shaped distribution called the 'diffraction envelope.'

The parameters that determine the angular dependence of the interference pattern are: first, the size of the aperture relative to the wavelength (here: a=3); second, the spacing d between the slits (here: d=3 a); and, of course, the number of slits. The three curves represent, respectively, the 1, 2, and 10 slits diffraction cases. The intensities have been normalizing in all instances of unity.
For the one slit case, you see there are some weak but discernible secondary lateral peaks. They reduce almost to the diffraction envelope.

For the two slits, as in the case of Young's double-slit experiment, we obtain more pronounced fringes. You can see how the one slit pattern 'envelops' the two slits pattern. However, notice that it would be incorrect to say, as you might frequently hear, that when we switch from the double slit to the single slit case, interference phenomena disappear. That is, in general, not the case. What happens is that we return to the envelope of the single slit, which contains many fewer fringes, but still might have some other interference fringes too (and in this case, it does). Again, interference is not a phenomenon specific to the double (or more) slits experiment.
Interference does not disappear if one slit is covered; it merely becomes weaker than it is with more slits.
Finally, in the case of 10 slits, the two slits curve turns out to be the envelope of the ten slits curve. So, you can observe how this is a more general trend and phenomenon which results from the interplay between diffraction and interference. Generally, the N-slits fringes and their spacing arise due to this combined effect between diffraction and interference.
These were only a few examples to outline, at least intuitively, how wave interference works.
A question we might ask is: What happens with a particle if we want to know its precise whereabouts in space? For example, let us determine the exact position of a particle by letting it go through a tiny pinhole, as

Isaac Newton did with photons in his investigations of the nature of light. If a particle goes through that single little hole on a piece of paper, we are authorized to say that we can determine its precise position in space. Because on the other hand, we identify that due to the wave- particle duality, we can't forget the particle's wavy aspect. When a particle, also a material particle, goes through this pinhole, it will likewise be diffracted and afterward, position itself on the detector screen according to an interference pattern.
If instead of dealing with slits, we take a tiny round hole of a size comparable to that of a few multiples of the wavelengths, we obtain circular interference fringes. It is an intrinsic and unavoidable effect on all types of waves.
The pinhole, as a detector of a particle's position, can't avoid interference.
If particles must link to a wave, according to the de Broglie relation, conceiving of it as a wave packet, we will always have the interference fringes, even with only one hole or slit and even with only one particle.
Compares the two cases in which the pinhole determines the position of the particle with an aperture of $a=2\lambda$ (high precision) and $a=20\lambda$ (low accuracy), with , as usual, the wavelength of the photon or, in case of a matter wave, the de Broglie wavelength.

If the pinhole is little, while it will decide the situation of a molecule with higher precision, it will likewise deliver a generally expansive diffraction design that delivers the area of the photon on the screen unsure. We can know in a generally exact way where the photon or matter molecule experienced the bit of paper inside the space- compelled by the pinhole's gap. However, it will be uprooted horizontally on the screen in any case because of diffraction and impedance marvels

Of course, with a single particle producing a single spot on the screen, no interference figure is visible. However, as we have learned with the

single-photon diffraction at the double slit, the probability of finding this spot is in one-to-one correspondence with the intensity of the interference fringes that many particles produce.

Moreover, recall also that we can't predict where precisely this spot will appear.

If instead, the pinhole is large, fringes will become less pronounced. We will know where the photon will hit the screen with relatively good accuracy, which means it 'felt' only a tiny displacement along with the screen.

However, by doing so, we will lose our capacity to determine where precisely the particle went through the pinhole, as it is no longer a pinhole at all, but a large hole. There is no way, never, not even in principle, to obtain the precise measurement of the particle position and, at the same time, avoid the production of interference fringes (or interference circles, as in the case of a circular aperture or significant diffraction effects). One will always obtain a more or less pronounced bell-shaped or peaked distribution of white spots on the screen. It is not because we don't have a sufficiently precise measurement apparatus but because it is a consequence of the intrinsic wave-nature of particles. It is a universal law of nature, according to which it is hopeless to believe that we can pass a wave through a slit and not observe any interference and diffraction phenomena.
Heisenberg's uncertainty principle explained using the single silt (or pinhole) diffraction experiment.
Now, this could also be interpreting as follows: The particle, once it has gone through the slit, will acquire an extra momentum, λp, along the vertical axis. It does not happen because of the interaction of an outside force or, as we might imagine, naively, by a communication, deviation, or bouncing effect of the particle with the slit's edges because, in that case, we would observe a random distribution but not an interference pattern. This extra momentum λp, which displaces the particle along

with the detection screen, is due only and exclusively to the wave nature of matter and light. We might interpret this also as a 'scattering' of the particle, but we should keep in mind that this is misleading terminology, as there is no scattering force at all. No scattering interaction of powers from the outside is necessary to make this happen.

Where does this extra amount of momentum λp come? It is merely the uncertainty we have about the particle's momentum in the first place. It is an inherent uncertainty of the properties of any particle due to their wave nature. It is the only possible conclusion if we want to avoid violating the principles of the conservation of momentum and energy.

The point is, we will never be able to determine with extreme precision

- That is, with an infinitely small slit of size λx=0 - without blurring the momentum because, by doing so, we will inevitably diffract the plane wavefront, the wavelength of which is given by the de Broglie's relation.

It will inevitably displace it according to a statistical law that reflects the diffraction and interference laws.

So, we must conclude that the smaller our uncertainty in determining the particle position (the size λx of the slit), the larger the diffraction effects and, therefore, the more significant the change over the momentum. (λp becomes large in the vertical direction.) On the other hand, if I want to know the particle's momentum with small uncertainty (λp small), we will have to open up the slit's aperture (λx large) to reduce the diffraction. However, I will never be able to determine with precision both the momentum and the position of a particle at the same time. We have to choose whether we want to keep focused on one or the other; never are we allowed to obtain both. Again, this is not because we are perturbing the system but because we are dealing with waves.

THE LAW OF ATTRACTION AND QUANTUM PHYSICS

The Law of Attraction has become a term for a family unit. It has become a trendy expression for those learning approaches to improve and upgrade life. Television infomercials, films, print

media, and tunes have gotten typical. Nonetheless, the motivation behind the law and its implementation are two things. The writing is brimming with understandings and clarifications of the reason for the law, yet excessively little endeavor has been made to depict the material science of the law.
Much has been learned about the meaning of the law and how it can be applied, but the world is still waiting for the mechanics of the law to demonstrate how to take advantage of it beyond merely keeping optimistic thoughts. What are the processes that make it work? Our efforts have centered on developing and designing resources that allow an individual to enforce the law more elegantly, effectively, and with less effort. What we discovered was a missing link on how to apply and execute this incredible fundamental theory of magnetism.
An examination into quantum mechanics has demonstrated that the demonstration of watching reality produces it. Endeavoring to recognize something permits nothing to show up. Similarly, if you don't know something, it doesn't exist in your abstract reality. The alleged misleading impact has demonstrated that positive or negative practices will create comparing impacts. Crafted by Dossey and others has indicated that petition affects whether the collector knows about it.

It is becoming progressively evident that we are co-creating our reality in the way we think and feel. In other words, in our unique and personal understanding of reality. We attract that which we consider as true into ourselves.

There is just a quantum of Energy as a stream of possible space positions and motions. This is omnipresent but, at the same time, none at all. There is no light and matter before something happens to make them "true," but what is that? Research has shown that this is something called the wave function collapse. And further investigation has revealed that to manifest reality is consciousness, which performs this action.
The wave function includes all the potential outcomes of a given situation, but only one occurs in the physical world when an attending consciousness collapses. For now, scientists are all peering over each other's heads watching the latest supercollider's event screen at Cern, Switzerland. They expect two protons to smash into each other, and, when they do, the screen shows an "episode," showing the release of all the subatomic particles that make them up. What they do not fathom is that their screen observation causes the wave functions to appear. Through witnessing what we want to manifest in our minds through imagination, inner listening, and a clear sense of our thoughts, we will learn to construct what we want. Likewise, we can resist the breakdown of possibilities into objects, events, and circumstances we don't wish to by refusing to give them our attention. A consciousness must Experience a parcel of Energy to be actual. Until that time, it lies enveloped on the other side of the quantum veil in the mystery of possibility. The "wave function" collapses when the Energy is Detected, making it measurable in the real world. Such particles can't be seen with the naked eye but only through advanced devices that can reveal where the particle was, along with the speed and position it was detected at the moment.

Because both consciousness and spirit exist in the spiritual realm on the other side of the veil, it makes sense that when we are in an inspired state or good mood, we can control our reality even better.

Once we are linked to Origin, we have more power in our own lives and our entire sphere of influence to create real and constructive change. Once we remain in that state of grace and reverence, trends arise, synchronicity increases, and people want to be around us and in that state of perfection want to join us. A positive wave function can more easily collapse while in this mode.

To stay in that state needs complete consciousness focus. The immediate knowledge of the divine, the one and all that leads to belief in the world that leads to the trust that is needed to step up to a higher- order level. We have to figure out how to fall just the positive, helpful wave capacities while removing our concentration from those prompting negative, harming impacts. A solitary individual's idea, discourse, and conduct can change the course of the worldwide network; all in all, this wonder of "watching" reality regularly applies to the next tangible instruments. At the point when you hear something from inside your internal voice, the soul of the real world or higher self, or sense something somewhere inside your very heart, you do something very similar when you see it ... you experience it. Experience is, along these lines, a more well-suited word to portray the genuine full presence of the activity of a wave breakdown. Also, stunningly better when the discernment can be multi-tactile. Seeing, hearing, and encountering an encounter brings about a condition of tactile reverberation, where all the tangible cycles are facilitated. A sound autonomic sensory system adds to a consolidated encountering profound unwinding and enormous innovativeness simultaneously (see the hypothesis of tactile reverberation).

We each have a section that is the creature and otherworldly. We are not one of these things, yet rather an awareness sandwiched in the middle of, whose task it is to pick between the choices offered by these two restricting essential components of ourselves and defeat the contention produced by the inconsistency between the polarities-recollect the old kid's shows where a darling shows up on one side with a little friend on the other? It's Life.

When a person creates his or her development and positive spiritual growth, he or she draws positive experience into him or herself. But when a person takes the wait and sees evolution approach, just sits around and "goes with the flow" by taking whatever is presented to them, they fall victim to the "strange attractor" or the chaos of nature that disassembles and demands rearrangement and reassembly to a higher level of order. The ancient Greeks, who believed he functioned as a ghost, called this cycle Ktisis to "unravel" everything not considered to be in order.
Nature does not rule the world and our lives; they are inherently disordered ... in chaos. Nevertheless, the four fundamental forces that physicists claim to materialize spirit have recently been redefined as celestial attractors that, over time, establish patterns of order. That is the real mystery of how reality expresses itself. Space is the original force that creates the universe by a point or singularity of zero dimensions. The time is used to chain the ends into the other attractors together.

An individual must become an attractor to make use of the Law of Attraction. Nevertheless, there are four attractor orders:

1. **The attractor of the 1st order Point** - leads one to be drawn into one specific task or to get trapped in a rut by being too concentrated on one idea or fixation.
2. **The 2nd order Cycle attractor** - allows one to get caught up in logical thought or an infinite loop that essentially repeats itself over and over again.
3. **The Tori attractor third request limit** - which is a positive development as it takes into consideration an intricate progression of Energy yet is to some degree obliged because of its semi periodicity.
4. **The 4th order Odd attractor**-which is the Absolute's chaotic behavior undoing everything that is not considered to be in order.

The accentuation, reason, and consistency of activity and articulation that one pays and makes choose the attractor where they fall. The best game-plan is to adjust oneself to the Torus attractor, direct it and compose one's whole vitality field in the imperatives of that dynamic topological space, which restricts it and permits it to turn out to be more intermittent and repeatable, permitting the combination of turbulent change sorted out and constrained by an equivalent measure of determinism. An individual may turn into a boundless toroid attractor bringing into what they need rather than just taking whatever the peculiar turbulent attractor has to bring to the table. This is the smoothed out nature of the Attraction Law and the key to its comprehension and execution.

Looking at a spectral-domain image of a time-domain object through eyes-open meditation and observing such attractors in action that reveal secret desires or intentions beyond the threshold of consciousness.
These pictures are deliberate palettes in which purpose can be visualized. All geometries and shapes have been shown to come from different ratios of real and imaginary partials that combine in the complex structure that makes up the wave function. Knowing this, and that spoken, or breathed speech is nothing more than a flow of these actual and imaginary elements, it becomes theoretically possible to learn how to draw what you want to see on the screen, hear what you want to hear on the headphones, feel what you want to feel inside, learn how to interact and direct the behavior of the automatons that make up all things.
The first step in learning to collapse the wave function is to perceive sense and experience what one thinks and feels on the inside. It, in turn, is the result of applying the law to attraction by studying how to connect with the ideal attractor while paying attention in the images to it. Utilizing a multi-tactile bi-stage approach which requires the client to turn into the specialist of their change by settling the distinction and pressure between the administrator and the machine, an extremity which can likewise be portrayed as player versus instrument, emotional versus

objective, real versus potential, or as the specialists know it as genuine versus nonexistent. These natural and nonexistent parts are called robots and are the least complex, most inseparable components or building squares of presence. We are both administrators and frameworks at the basest basic degree of nature. Change by then will permit us the capacity to set up the second and, for all time, adjust their lives. The exemplification and final destiny of the breakdown of the wave system are to accomplish intermingling among players and instruments.

PHOTOELECTRIC EFFECT:

EINSTEIN'S THEORY

When electromagnetic radiation of appropriate frequency is made to hit the surface of metal like, say, sodium, electrons are emitted from the metal. This phenomenon of emission
of electrons from certain materials (which include several metals and semiconductors) by electromagnetic radiation is referred to as the photoelectric effect. This effect can be demonstrated and studied with the help of a set-up like the one shown in Figure 1.1.

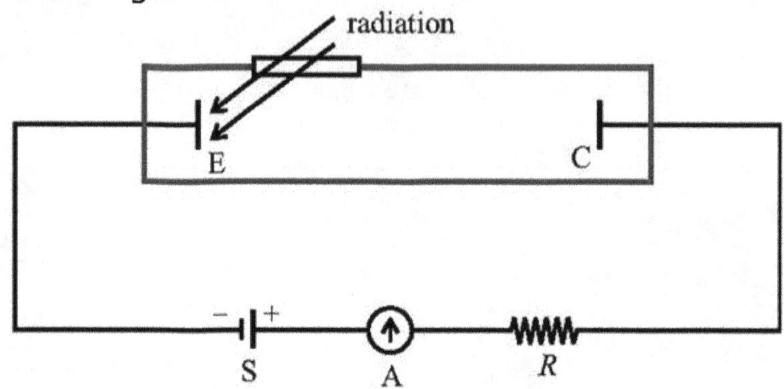

Figure 1.1: Set-up to study and analyze photoelectric effect; E is the emitting surface while C is the collecting electrode; A is a current- measuring device; S is a DC voltage source whose polarity can be reversed; R denotes a resistor; the actual circuit may not be as simple as shown here.

A metallic emitting electrode (E) and a collecting electrode (C) are enclosed in an evacuated chamber in which a window admits electromagnetic radiation of appropriate frequency to fall on E. A circuit made up of a source of EMF (S), a resistor (R), and a sensitive current-meter (A) is established between E and C. The polarity of S can be changed so that C can be either at a higher or a lower potential concerning E.

FEATURES OF PHOTOELECTRIC EMISSION

This arrangement can be used to record several exciting features of photoelectric emission. If for a given intensity of the incident radiation, the potential (V) of C to E is positive, then all the electrons emitted from E are collected by C, and A records a current (I). This current remains almost constant when V is increased because all the photoelectrons are collected by C whenever V is flattering. This is known as the saturation current for the given intensity of the incident radiation.
However, this entire phenomenon of a current being recorded due to the emission of photoelectrons from E is dependent on the frequency (v) of the radiation.
If the frequency is sufficiently low, then photoelectric emission does not occur, and no photo-current is recorded. For the time being, we accept that the frequency is high enough for photoelectric emission to take place, and refer back to Figure 1.1.

If holding the frequency and intensity of the radiation constant, one now reverses the polarity of S and records the photocurrent with increasing magnitude of V. One finds that the photo-current persists but decreases gradually till it becomes zero for a value V = −Vs of the potential of C concerning E. The magnitude (Vs) of V for which the photocurrent becomes zero is termed the stopping potential for the given frequency of the incident radiation. This is shown graphically in fig. 1.1.
The lower of the two curves shown in Figure 1.2 describes this variation of I with V for a given intensity (J1) of the incident radiation, and the frequency v being also held constant at a sufficiently high value.

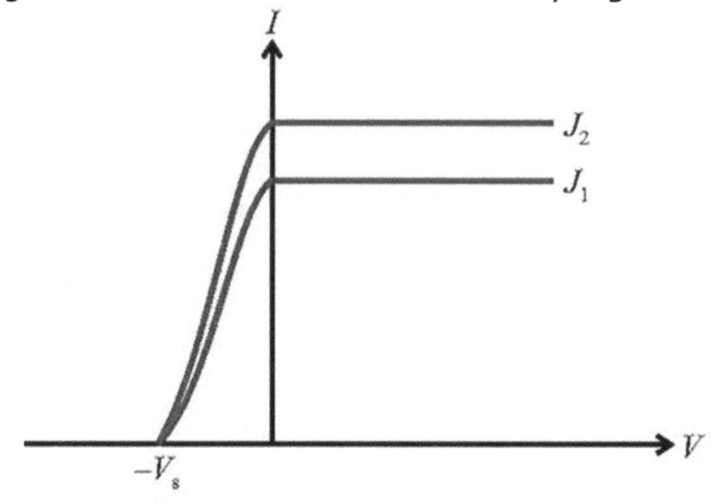

Figure 1.1: Graphical representation of the characteristics of photoelectric emission; variation of photocurrent I with applied voltage V is shown for two values of intensity of radiation, J1, and J2 (> J1), while the frequency v is held constant; the stopping potential Vs is independent of power.

If, now, the experiment is repeated for some other value, say, J2, of the intensity of radiation, then one obtains a similar variation, as in the upper curve of fig. 1.1, but with a different value of the saturation current, the latter being higher for J2 > J1. However, the stopping potential does not depend on the intensity since, as seen in the figure, both the curves give the same value of the stopping potential.
On the other hand, if the testing is repeated with different values of the frequency, keeping the intensity fixed, one finds that the stopping potential increases with frequency (Figure 1.2). One finds that, if the frequency is made to decrease, the stopping potential reduces to zero at some finite value (say, v0) of the frequency. This value of the frequency (v0) is found to be a characteristic of the emitting material and is referred to as the threshold frequency of the latter. Indeed, no photoelectric emission from the material under consideration can take place unless the frequency of the incident radiation is higher than the threshold frequency. Moreover, for v > v0, photoelectric emission does take place for arbitrarily small values of the intensity. The effect of lowering the intensity is simply to decrease the photo-current, without stopping the emission altogether.

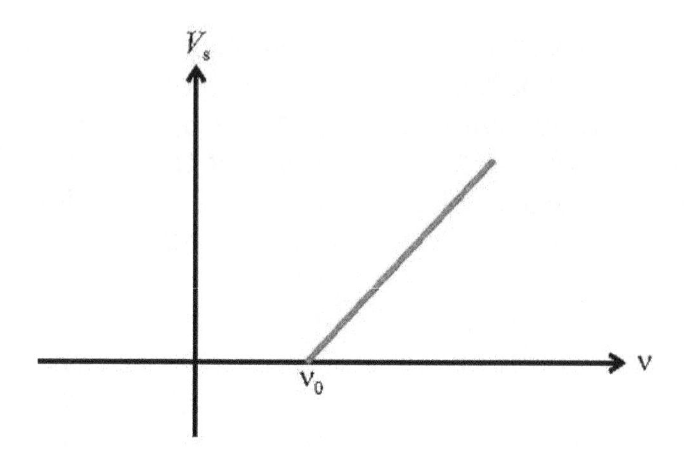

Figure 1.2: Variation of stopping potential with frequency; no photoelectric emission takes place if the frequency is less than the threshold value v0, however large the intensity may be.

THE ROLE OF PHOTONS IN PHOTOELECTRIC EMISSION

All these observed features of photoelectric emission could not be accounted for by the classical theory. For instance, classical theory tells us that whatever be the frequency, photoelectric emission should occur if the intensity of radiation is high enough since, for a high intensity of radiation, electrons within the emitting material should receive sufficient energy to come out, overcoming their binding force.
It was Einstein who first gave a complete account of the observed features of the photoelectric effect by invoking the idea of the photon as a quantum of energy, as introduced by Planck in connection with his derivation of the black body spectrum formula.
While the photons in the black body radiation were the energy quanta associated with standing wave modes, similar considerations apply to propagate radiation as well. Indeed, the components of electric and magnetic field intensities of propagating monochromatic electromagnetic radiation vary sinusoidally with time. Once again, a propagating mode of the field can be looked upon as a quantum mechanical harmonic oscillator of frequency, say, v. The minimum value by which the energy of the radiation can increase or decrease is once again hv, and this increase or decrease can once again be described as the appearance or disappearance of an energy quantum, or a photon, of frequency v. Such a photon associated with a progressive wave mode, moreover, carries a momentum just like any other particle such as an electron (by contrast, an energy quantum of black body radiation has no net rate). The terminologies for energy and momentum of a photon of frequency v are the de Broglie relations by now familiar to us:

where λ stands for the wavelength of the propagating monochromatic radiation and where only the magnitude of the momentum has been considered. When monochromatic radiation of frequency v is made to be incident on the surface of a metal or a semiconductor, photons of the same frequency interact with the material, and some of these exchange energy with the electrons in it. This can be interpreted as collisions between the photons and the electrons, where the power of the photon engaged in a crash is transferred to the electron. This energy transfer may be sufficient to knock the electron out of the material, which is how photoelectric emission takes place.

BOUND SYSTEMS AND BINDING ENERGY

A metal or a semiconductor is a crystalline material where a large number of atoms are arranged in a regular periodic structure. Electrons in such material are bound with the entire crystalline structure. In this context, it is essential to grasp the concept of a bound system. For instance, a small piece of paper glued on to board makes up a set system, and it takes some energy to tear the piece of paper away from the board.

If the power of the network made up of the paper separated from the board be taken as zero (in the process of energy accounting, anyone energy can be given a pre-assigned value, since power is undetermined to the extent of an additive constant), and if the energy required to tear the paper apart be E, then the principle of conservation of energy tells us that the power of the bound system with the paper glued on to the board must have been −E since the tearing energy E added to this initial energy gives the final power 0.

As another instance of a bound system, consider a hydrogen atom made up of an electron 'glued' to a proton by the attractive Coulomb force between the two. Once again, it takes energy to knock the electron out of the atom, thereby yielding an unbound electron separated from the proton. The power of the divided system, with both the proton and the electron at rest, is taken to be zero by convention, in which case the expression gives the energy of the bound hydrogen atom with the electron in the nth stationary state. Notice that this energy is a negative quantity, which means that positive energy of equal magnitude is necessary to tear the electron away from the proton. This method of knocking an electron out of an atom is known as ionization. It can be accomplished with the help of a photon, which supplies the necessary energy to the electron, and the process is termed photo-ionization.
In an exactly similar manner, a hydrogen molecule is a bound system made up of two protons and two electrons. Looking at any one of these electrons, one can say that it is not bound to any one of the two protons but the pair of protons together. Indeed, the two electrons are shared by the pair of protons and form what is known as a covalent bond between the protons. Once again, it takes some energy to knock any one of these electrons out of the hydrogen molecule.
The minimum energy necessary to separate the components of a bound system is termed its binding energy. On receiving this amount of energy, the components get separated from each other, without acquiring any kinetic energy in the separated configuration. If the bound system receives an amount of energy greater than the binding energy, then the

extra amount goes to generate kinetic energy in the components. In this context, an interesting result relates to the situation when one of the components happens to be much lighter than the other. In this case, the extra energy is used up almost entirely as the kinetic energy of the lighter component. Incidentally, when I speak of a bound system, I tacitly imply that it is to be looked at as a system made of two components. The same system may be looked at as one made up of more than two components as well. For instance, in the example of the piece of paper glued on to the board, the components I have in mind are the paper and the board. But, given a sufficient supply of energy, the board can also be broken up into two or more pieces, and then one would have to think of a system made up of more than two components. Indeed, the board and the piece of paper are made up of a large number of molecules, and the molecules can all be torn away from one another. Similarly, all of the two electrons and the two protons making up the hydrogen molecule can be pulled away from one another, for which a different amount of energy would be required as compared to the energy required to yield just one electron separated from an ion. This latter we term the binding energy of the electron in the hydrogen molecule.

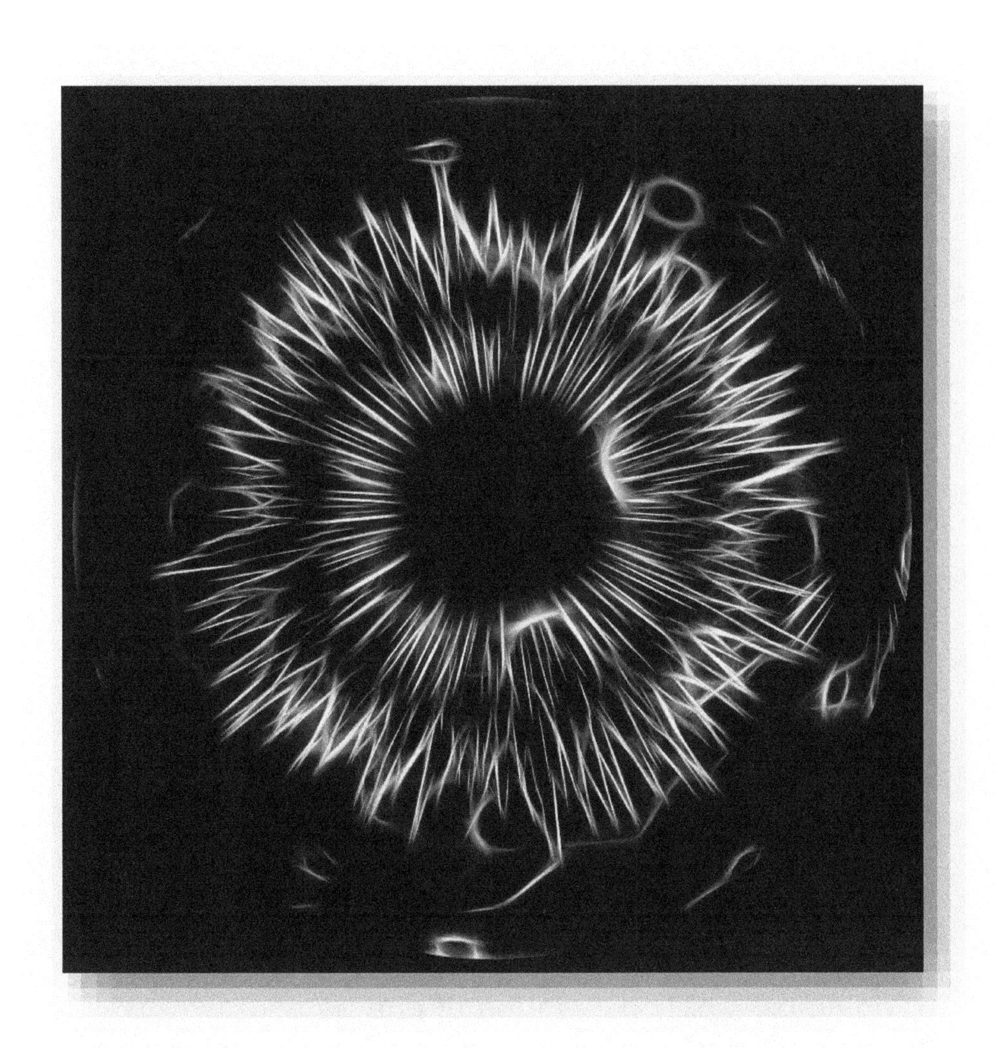

EVOLUTION OF ELEMENTARY PARTICLES

The author believes that the universe was first created not as elements of the larger nucleus but as elementary and sub elementary particles. An electron and a proton attracted each
other, forming the primitive hydrogen atom. At a stage, hydrogen atoms fused through a fusion reaction, forming heavier elements.
Contrary to the big bang theory, what happened at the time of the big bang 13.7 billion years ago, or maybe earlier; rather than the whole universe came into being, only two particles of opposite and equal momenta exited the speed-of-light reference frame along the axis of motion of the sonic reference frame. Their exit was in opposite directions such that one particle was in the direction of motion of the reference frame while the other was in the opposite direction. The equal and opposite momenta ensure that no disturbance (recoil) occurring at the point of exit. Because the sonic reference frame is inertial from the perspective of this reference frame, mass, time, and length measures are finite as calculated from inside this sonic frame.
All laws of physics are official inside this sonic system, including laws of conservation of energy and momentum. The exit of the two particles from the sonic system is implemented according to the laws of conventional mechanics as considered from the inside of that reference frame.

THE LAWS OF ENERGY AND MOMENTUM ARE

CONSERVED AT THE MOMENT OF EXIT.

An observer hypothetically situated at an observation post at rest to observe, monitor, and measure the sequence of events of the two particles' as they exit from the sonic reference frame, up to their final destinations. The hypothetical situation at rest is assumed because the very first particles' exit occurs in zero space. Before the particles' exit, the at-rest observer will not be able to detect the two particles when they are in the speed-of-light reference frame. Conferring to the theory of special relativity, an observer at rest detects the sonic reference frame and its contents as a point in space with zero volume and infinite mass. As the two particles exit the speed-of-light reference frame, the observation post now detects and finds that the forward and reverse particles have a speed faster and slower than the speed of light, respectively. This is because both particles left the speed-of-light reference frame in opposite directions: one in the forward (faster) direction and the other in the reverse direction (slower). Both particles are now visible to the observation post at rest because both have real velocities propagating in the same space, as explained earlier.

After the two particles exit from the sonic reference outline, they apply a push to pull in one another, trying to connect to come back to their ground state, which is the speed of light. Since the two particles presently are in the subsonic and supersonic reference outlines, they can't reemerge the speed-of-light boundary. Their taboo reemergence is because their masses increment as they approach the speed of light once more. The weighty masses need truly impressive vitality to arrive at the sonic speed which they need. Incapable of reemerging the sonic reference outline, the two particles arriving at a specific good ways from one another and afterward stop. In this position, they have depleted the greater part of the vitality they got from the sonic reference outline. The supersonic molecule is presently at supersonic speed while the subsonic molecule came to relative rest. The moving supersonic molecule remains at a fixed good ways from the subsonic molecule while holding its

supersonic speed. The main opportunities for the supersonic molecule to keep a fixed separation and the speed it has is around way around the subsonic molecule. On the off chance that we indicate that the supersonic molecule is the electron and that the subsonic molecule is the proton, at that point, we can announce the introduction of the hydrogen iota. The hydrogen iota is framed with the proton at the focal point of a roundabout way shaped by the moving electron with supersonic speed.

The previous arrangement of occasions completed by the two particles after their takeoff from the sonic reference edge may prompt three significant ends: (1) In their push to recombine to come back to their ground state, it isn't more than the electrostatic fascination between the proton and electron. (2) The supersonic mass rotating around the subsonic mass isn't more than the arrangement of the hydrogen particle with the electron spinning around the proton. (3) Their fascination stops at a fixed separation that is restricted by their expansion in mass, which characterizes the nuclear sweep. At the observation post at rest, an observer detects the formation of a hydrogen atom in an inflated space. From the observation post perspective, the newly formed hydrogen atom and inflated space came from nowhere or nothing, because the sonic reference frame is an abstract location as observed from rest. This may answer the controversial question, "Can something come from nothing?" The answer is yes; something can come from an unobserved location.

The two exited particles are now the electron and the proton. The question nowadays is, "Why have we decided that the electron is the supersonic mass and the proton is the subsonic mass?" The answer is simple; because the electron, because of its supersonic speed, is always in continuous motion and never been found to be at rest, it must be the supersonic particle. The proton can be found at rest; therefore, it must be the subsonic particle.

The evolution of space and the simplest element, the hydrogen atom, is

the earliest step toward the universe's formation and evolution. The

author believes that hydrogen was the earliest constituent of the cosmos. As a result, the evolution of the hydrogen atom and space is the first step toward the evolution of the universe.
The following is a formal presentation of the theory of the evolution of elementary particles.

POSTULATES

To continue with the turn of events and the development of elementary particles, the accompanying hypothesizes might be embraced:

1. Inertial reference outlines exist at any speed, including slower, quicker, or the speed of light.
2. Inside any inertial reference outline, life is typical, and all laws of material science are substantial.
3. Masses can leave the speed-of-light reference outline at quicker or more slow speeds. However, they can't come back to that speed (single direction exit).

As indicated by old-style material science, inertial reference casings can exist at any speed. Consequently, the proposed one is following Galilean and Newtonian traditional material science. The hypothesis of special relativity didn't preclude the likelihood that an inertial reference edge can exist at the speed of light. This hypothesis only expressed that such a reference edge couldn't quicken to that speed, and such a reference outline can't be identified from rest. This hypothesis of special relativity discloses to us that a sonic reference casing could exist at the speed of light with the requirement that this reference outline initially existed at that speed, and it didn't quicken from slower or quicker than the speed of light. Then again, no law in material science rejects the presence of a reference outline over the speed of light. Along these lines, the proposed one could be received.
Postulate two is in line with all classical laws of physics as long as the reference frame is nonaccelerating or inertial.

Postulate three complies with the Lorentz mass transformation equation can be rewritten as

$$m = m'\sqrt{1-\frac{v^2}{c^2}} \qquad (C.6')$$

Where:
m′ is the mass in the sonic reference frame at the moment of departure,
m is the mass as measured in the subsonic or supersonic reference frames,is the velocity of the particle, and c is the velocity of light.
The equation states that as the velocity of a particle departs from the speed of light (faster or slower), the particle's mass, m, is reduced to a smaller mass, as measured from rest. The reader can easily verify that a particle cannot reenter the speed of the light reference frame because its mass becomes infinitely large, according to the equation.
Consequently, particles can easily exit the sonic speed in both directions, above or below. Because of its nearly infinite mass, as a particle's speed increases toward the speed of light, that particle is forbidden to reenter that speed. As a result, masses can have an easy transition from sonic to subsonic or supersonic speeds while the reverse is forbidden. In general, the sonic reference frame exit is a one-way process. Therefore, postulate three is valid and may be adopted.

EVOLUTION OF THE HYDROGEN ATOM

The preceding discussion of the ejection of the two equal momentum masses poses a striking resemblance to the creation of the electron/proton pair. The supersonic and the subsonic ejected particles are the electron and the proton, respectively, because of the following:

1. As observed from rest, the ejected supersonic particle is a negative imaginary term. The negative term may be related to the electrostatic charge of this mass. The supersonic particle resembles the electron because of its continuous motion.
2. The subsonic ejected particle's mass is positive and real and attracts
the supersonic mass; then, it must be the proton.
3. The imaginary term associated with supersonic mass could be related to the difference between the texture and the entity of the two ejected masses.
4. The attraction between the negative supersonic mass and the subsonic positive mass, in their effort to return to their ground state, is evidence of the attractive electrostatic forces of the two ejected masses.
5. The two evolved masses cannot fuse because such an action requires that the created masses must reenter the sonic reference frame, which is forbidden according to postulate three.

It can be generalized that the two ejected mass is not more than an electron and a proton. Their attraction up to a certain distance and the electron's continuous motion around the proton is strong evidence of hydrogen atom formation. The fixed radius between the electron and the proton explains why the electron does not fuse with the proton in the hydrogen atom disregarding the strong electrostatic attractive forces. Let us now modify our above assumption of the spaceship. Assume that because of a new action at the sonic reference frame, at the other dimension or maybe at a black hole, a sonic mass split into two masses. The two masses obtain energy to split and exit their sonic home with equal and opposite momentum along the direction of motion of the sonic reference frame. The two split particles are the electron and the proton forming the earliest hydrogen atom.

QUANTUM COMPUTING

IS INFORMATION PHYSICAL?

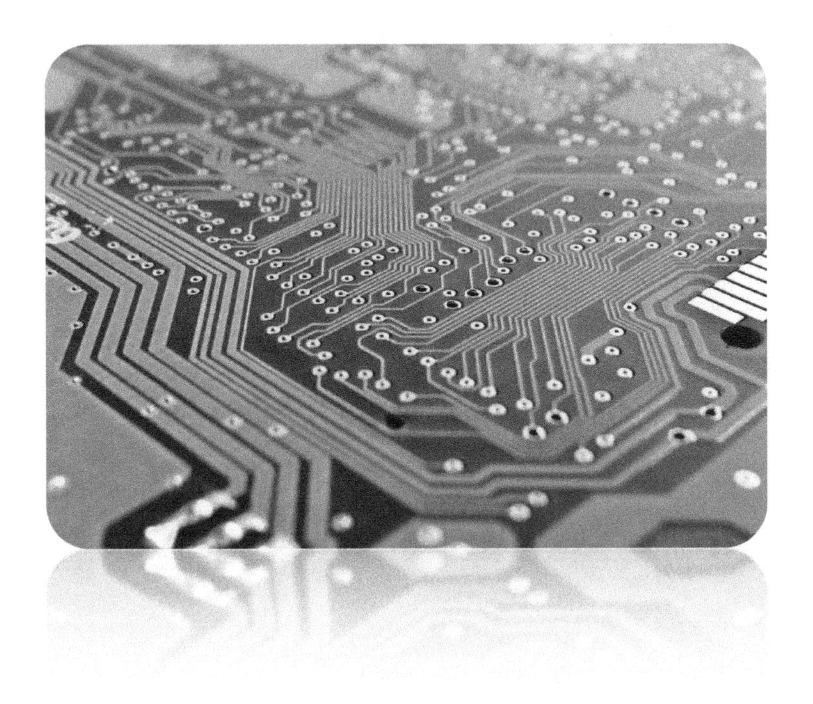

Computers are devices that process information. Computer scientist and physicist Rolf Landauer argued that knowledge is a part of the physical world.

He elaborated this as follows:
Data is not a disembodied abstract entity; it is always linked to physical representation. It is represented by engraving on a stone tablet, a [magnetic] turn, a [electrical] charge, a hole in a punched card, a mark on paper, or some other equivalents. This links the handling of information with all the possibilities and limitations of our actual physical world, its laws of physics, and its storage of available parts. If "information is physical," as Landauer has said, then it would seem necessary to treat it mechanically. In other words, the physical means by which information is stored and interpreted by computers should be considered using quantum theory. It helps to understand computation in general before addressing quantum computers.

WHAT IS A COMPUTER?

A computer is a machine that receives and stores information input, processes the information according to a programmable sequence of steps, and produces the resulting output of information. The term 'computer' was used for the first time in the 1600s to refer to people who perform calculations or computations and now refers to computers that compute. Computing machines can be divided roughly into four types:

1. Computing devices for classical computational physics. These machines use moving parts, including levers and gears, to perform computing. Usually, they are not programmable, but always perform the same operation, such as adding numbers. An example is the 1905 Burroughs Adding Machine.
2. Electromechanical classical mechanics fully programmable computing devices. These machines operate using electronically controlled moving parts. They process information stored as digital bits represented by the locations of a large number of electromechanical switches.

The first such machine was built in 1941 by Konrad Zuse in wartime Germany. In theory, their programmability allows them to solve any problem that can be found and overcome by using algebra. These were the first 'universal' computers in this context.

3. All-electronic, hybrid quantum-classical – physics computers. These fully programmable, universal computing machines have no moving mechanical parts and work using electronic circuits. The first to be constructed was the ENIAC, engineered by John Mauchly and J. Presper Eckert, University of Pennsylvania, 1946. The physical principles that describe the motion of electrons in these circuits are rooted in quantum physics. But, given that there are no superposition states or entangled states involving electrons in different circuit components (capacitors, transistors, etc.), classical physics adequately describes how electrons represent information. Therefore, we call these machines—essentially any computer in operation today—'classic computers.'

4. Quantum computers. If ever built successfully, these devices would operate according to the principles of quantum physics. Knowledge will be expressed by the quantum states of individual electrons or other elementary quantum artifacts, and there will be entangled states involving electrons in various circuit components. These computers are expected to be able to solve those kinds of problems much faster than any modern classical computer can do.

HOW DO COMPUTERS WORK?

Computers store and manipulate information using a binary alphabet language consisting of only two symbols: 0 and 1. Every 1 or 0 symbols is referred to as a bit, short for a binary digit because it can take one of two possible values. A page of text, such as the one you read, is represented in a computer file as a long string of numbers. A binary code represents every letter. For example, 'A' becomes 01000001, 'B' becomes 01000001, and so on.

In a typical computer, each bit is represented by the number of electrons stored in a small device called a capacitor. We can think of a capacitor as a box that holds a certain number of electrons, sort of like a bulk grain bin in a food store that holds a certain amount of rice. Each capacitor is called a memory cell. For example, such a capacitor could have a maximum capacity of 1,000 electrons. If the capacitor is full or almost full of electrons, we say it represents a bit of a value of 1. If the capacitor is empty or almost empty, we say it represents a bit value of 0. The capacitor is not allowed to be half-filled, and the circuitry is designed to ensure that this does not happen.
Through grouping together eight capacitors, each of which is either full or empty, any eight- bit number — e.g., 01110011—can be interpreted.
The role of the machine circuitry is to empty or fill various capacitors according to a set of rules called a program. Eventually, the action of filling and emptying the capacitors manages to perform the desired calculation — say, to add two 8-bit numbers. In a computer, the steps are performed by tiny components of computer circuitry called logic gates. A logic gate is made of silicon and other elements arranged in a way that either blocks or passes electrical charge, depending on its electrical environment. Logic gate inputs are bit values, represented by a full capacitor (a 1) or an empty capacitor (a 0). (The word 'gate' is associated with the fact that something goes into it and something comes out of it.)

HOW SMALL CAN A SINGLE LOGIC GATE BE?

In the first all-electronic computers, such as the ENIAC, built in the 1940s, a single logic gate was a vacuum tube similar to the amplifier tubes still used today in vintage-style electric guitar amplifiers. Each box has at least the size of your thumb. By 1970, the microcircuit revolution was able to reduce the size of each gate to about one-hundredth of a millimeter. When things get much smaller than this, it's best to measure the length of a unit called a nanometer, which is equal to one-millionth of a millimeter. The size of the gate in 1970 was 10,000 nanometers. On the other hand, a single silicon atom, which is the main atomic element in computer circuitry, is around 0.2 nanometer in thickness. By 2012, available gates in typical computers had been reduced enough so that they could be spaced apart by as little as 22 nanometers — that is, only about a hundred atoms apart. The actual working area of the gate was less than 2.2 nanometers of ten atoms in thickness. This small size allows you to place a few billion memory locations and entrances in an area the size of your thumbnail.

Having gate sizes much smaller than those dimensions leads to both a curse and a blessing. We leave the domain of many-atomic physics and enter the realm of single-atomic physics. There are now variations between the classical physics principles that sufficiently explain the average behavior of many atoms and the quantum physics principles that are required when dealing with single atoms. We reach a random action domain that doesn't sound good if we're trying to get a well- regulated system to do our numerical bidding. In reality, a group of scientists led by Michelle Simmons, director of the Center for Quantum Computation and Communication at the University of New South Wales, Australia, constructed a gate consisting of a single phosphorus atom embedded in a silicon crystal tube. This is the smallest gate ever to be designed. This gate only functions appropriately if cooled to shallow temperature: - 459 degrees Fahrenheit (- 273 degrees Celsius). If the material is not at least as cold, the random (thermal) motion of

the silicon atoms in the crystal decreases the confinement of the electron psi wave, which may leak out of the channel into which it is intended to be confined. For day-to-day desktop computers, which, after all, have to operate at room temperature, this leakage prevents such single-atom gates from being the basis of the technology that everyone can use. On the other hand, these experiments demonstrate that computers can, at least in theory, be built on the atomic scale, where quantum physics rules.

CAN WE CREATE COMPUTERS THAT USE FUNDAMENTALLY QUANTUM BEHAVIOR?

Given that physics defines the ultimate behavior and efficiency of information transfer, storage, and processing, it is reasonable to ask how quantum physics plays a role in information technology.

Because electronic computers rely on the behavior of electrons, and communication systems rely on the behavior of photons — both elementary particles — it is not surprising that quantum physics ultimately determines the performance of information technology. But here is subtlety.

Computer technologies currently in use do not involve quantum superposition states to represent information. They use conditions that can be considered classical forms of physical things — namely, groups of electrons.
The big question is: can we create computers that use quantum- mechanical states to enhance our ability to solve real-world problems? If these computers were ever built, they would be able to bypass certain forms of data encryption methods much faster than any computer that is operating today.
This would revolutionize the field of privacy and confidentiality for computers and the Internet. The encryption key that might take thousands of years to crack using a conventional computer could only take minutes on a quantum computer.

WHAT IS A QUBIT?

The word bit is used to refer to both the abstract, disembodied mathematical concept of information and the physical entity that embodies the info. It is evident in classical physics that a 'physical bit' carries one 'abstract bit' of knowledge. There is a straightforward one- to-one relationship between the state of the physical bit and the value of the abstract bit, 0 or 1. We may also use individual quantum artifacts, such as an electron or a photon, to incarnate a portion. In this case, the elementary physical entity is called a qubit, short for 'quantum bit.' A qubit has two different quantum states, such as the H and V polarization of the photon, or the upper path and the lower path of the electron. When measured, the results represent a bit value of 0 or 1. But remember that we can select different polarization measurement schemes — say, H/V or D/A. The results may then be random, with the probability of observing possible outcomes depending on which measurement scheme we selected. In this case, there is no one-to-one relation between the state of the physical qubit and the value of some abstract conceptual bit. The concepts of quantum physics suggest significant variations between the behavior of classical bits and qubits. Classical bits can be copied as many times as we want, without any degradation of the information; qubits cannot be copied or cloned even once, although they can be teleported. The state of the classical bit, 0 or 1, can be determined by a single measurement; any sequence of measures cannot select the quantum state of the single qubit.

WHAT PHYSICAL PRINCIPLES DIFFERENTIATE CLASSICAL AND QUANTUM COMPUTERS APART?

There are considerable differences between the types of gates used in classical computers and the gates that need to be used in quantum computers. Classical gates perform operations that are not reversible; understanding the output does not tell you what the inputs are. On the other hand, if a quantum gate is to operate correctly with qubits, it must be reversible. That is, you need to be able to determine the input states by understanding the output states.

This requirement arises because any quantum gate operation must be a unit process.

TEST REALIZATION OF QUANTUM COMPUTER

The engineering straightforwardness makes the quantum computer quicker, littler, and less expensive be that as it may, its reasonable complexities are presenting troublesome problems for its test acknowledgment. Various endeavors have been made toward this path with a 20 empowering achievement. It is envisaged that it may not be too far when the quantum computer would supplant an advanced computer with its full possibilities. A portion of the endeavors for the trial acknowledgment of quantum computer is abridged as follows:

HETEROPOLYMERS:

The first heteropolymer based quantum computer was planned and worked in 1988 by Teich and afterward improved by Lloyd in 1993. In a heteropolymer computer, a direct exhibit of particles is utilized as memory cells. Data is put away on a cell by siphoning the relating particle into an energized state. Guidelines are transmitted to the heteropolymer by laser beats of fittingly tuned frequencies. The idea of the calculation that is performed on the chosen iotas is controlled by the shape and the span of the beat.

ION TRAPS:

A particle trap quantum computer was first proposed by Cirac and Zoller in 1995 and executed first by Monroe and partners in 1995 and afterward by Schwarzchild in 1996. The particle trap computer encodes information in vitality conditions of particles and vibrational modes between the particles. Theoretically, every particle is worked by a different laser. A fundamental analysis exhibited that Fourier changes can be assessed with the particle trap computer. This, like this, prompts Shor's considering calculation, which is based on Fourier changes.

QUANTUM ELECTRODYNAMICS CAVITY:

The Quantum electrodynamics (QED) depression PC was appeared by Turchette and partners in 1995. The PC comprises of a QED pit loaded up with some cesium particles and a game-plan of lasers, stage move identifiers, polarizer additionally, mirrors. The plan is a genuine quantum PC since it can make, control, additionally, ensure superposition and traps.

NUCLEAR MAGNETIC RESONANCE:

A Nuclear Magnetic Resonance (NMR) PC comprises a case stacked up with liquid and an NMR machine. Each iota in the liquid is a free quantum memory register. Count proceeds by sending radio pulses to the test and scrutinizing its response. Qubits are realized as turn states of the centers of particles involving the iotas. In an NMR PC, the readout of the memory register is practiced by an assessment performed on a factual outfit of state, 2.7x10 19 particles.
This is instead of the QED pit PC molecule trap PC, in which a singular, separated quantum system was used for memory register.
NMR PC can illuminate NP (Non-polynomial) complete issues in polynomial time. Most practical achievements in quantum processing so far have been cultivated using NMR PCs.

QUANTUM DOTS

Quantum PCs reliant on quantum spot innovation use more clear designing and less advanced test, theoretical and mathematical capacities when appeared differently about the four quantum PC use referenced as of recently. An assortment of quantum bits, wherein the touches are related to their nearest neighbors by the techniques for gated tunneling limits, are used for making quantum portals using a split entryway method.

This plans one of the central focuses: the qubits are controlled electrically. The weakness of this design is that quantum touches can talk with their nearest neighbors simply coming about data readout is problematic.

JOSEPHSON JUNCTIONS

The Josephson crossing point quantum PC was shown in 1999 by Nakamura, also the partners. In this PC, a Cooper pair box, which is a touch of superconducting island anode, is weakly coupled to a mass superconductor. Weak coupling between the superconductors makes a Josephson convergence between them, which carries on as a capacitor. If the Cooper box is little as a quantum bit, the charging current breaks into the discrete move of individual Cooper sets, so finally, it is possible to move a singular Cooper pair over the convergence just. Like quantum touch, PCs in Josephson convergence PCs, qubits are controlled electrically. Josephson's crossing point's quantum PCs are one of the promising opportunities for future progressions.

THE KANE COMPUTER

This PC seems to be like a quantum spot PC, yet indifferent habits, it is more similar to an NMR PC. It comprises of a singular appealingly unique center of p 31in a pearl of isotopically spotless, alluringly inert Si 28. The model is then set in a particularly strong, alluring field to set the turn of p 31equal or antiparallel with the direction of the field. The turn of the p31core would then have the option to be constrained by applying a radio repeat heartbeat to a control anode, called An entryway, neighboring the center.

Electron interceded correspondence between turns could this way be constrained by applying a voltage to terminals called J-doors, set between the p 31cores.

TOPOLOGICAL QUANTUM COMPUTER

The idea behind the topological quantum PC is to use the plait pack properties that depict the development of anyons to finish quantum computations. It is declared that such a PC should be impervious to quantum missteps of the topological quality of anyons.

FIVE MODERN APPLICATION OF QUANTUM PHYSICS

The concept of Quantum Physics is difficult and strange. Understanding the activities of tiny particles and trying to define the forces that made them work led Albert Einstein and
his colleagues into an argument about the subject. The issue with Quantum Physics is that it has a very strange concept that defies common sense notions on causality, locality, and realism. Realism makes us know that something exists- we could know the sun exists even without staring at the sun.
Causality explains that something happens because something caused it to. Flicking the switch of a light bulb and we see the light, that's causality. Due to the speed of light, when we strike a match, the light doesn't take a million light-years to come on; this is all dependent on the location. All of these principles are not followed in the quantum realm. It's a whole different world there.
One clear example of this is the quantum entanglement, and this states that particles on opposite sides of the universe can be entangled to exchange knowledge instantly. This was a concept Einstein couldn't accept. In the year 1964, a physicist by the name John Stewart Bell was able to prove that quantum physics was a complete and workable theory. He was able to define Bell's Theorem.

The Bell theory proposed some series of inequality, now referred to as the Bell inequality; this series represented how measurements of the spin of a particle A and Particle B would be distributed if they were not entangled. While the experiment was being carried out, and after it was

carried out, it was discovered that Bell's inequality was violated. He has been able to show that quantum properties like entanglement are as real as staring at a tree.
And in this time, the various strange concepts of Quantum Physics have been applied to develop different systems with real-world applications.

5 OF THE MOST EXCITING ONES:

1. Ultra-Precise Clocks

The need to have a reliable timepiece with precision is very necessary. Times are already synchronizing the technological world; the time helps to keep the stock markets as well as maintain the GPS systems. The standard clocks we know make use of frequent oscillations of physical artifacts such as pendulums or quartz crystals to create their 'ticks' and 'tocks.'
In today's world, the most accurate clocks make use of theories of Quantum mechanics to calculate time. They monitor the specific frequency of radiation, which is required to make electrons jump between energy levels.
The Quantum logic clock, which is located at the US National Institute of Standards and Technology (NIST) in Colorado, only gains or loses a second every 3.7 billion years. The NIST strontium clock, which was revealed not so long ago, will remain accurate for the period of five billion years, a time longer than the Earth's current age.
The importance of this super-accurate and sensitive clock cuts across different areas: telecommunications, GPS navigation, and surveying. The precision of these atomic clocks partially depends on the number of atoms being used.
When scientists try to cram about a hundred more atoms into an atomic clock, this will make the accuracy of the clock about ten times more.

2. Uncrackable Codes

In the traditional form of cryptography, keys were used to make it work. The sender of the secret message uses a particular kind of key to encode the information, and the recipient of the information will be able to use another key to decode the information or message. However, the risk that this message can still be picked is one that cannot be taken for granted. To solve this problem, technologists have employed the use of a theoretically unbreakable distribution of the quantum key (QKD). In QKD, done polarized photons are used to send the main information. This limits the photon; this makes it vibrate in just a singular plane -it could be up and down or left to right.
The other party accepting this data would then be able to utilize captivated channels to unscramble the key and afterward utilize the picked calculation to scramble the message appropriately. Individual information is as yet sent over typical correspondence channels, yet one can just disentangle the message except if they have the specific quantum key. The quantum decides to give that "perusing" enraptured photons will consistently change their states, and any push to listen in will alarm the communicators about security penetrate. On this day, organizations, for example, Toshiba, BBN Technologies, and ID Quantique, utilize the QKD to plan super safe systems. In 2007, Switzerland had the option to embrace an ID Quantique item to give a carefully designed democratic framework in their races. In 2004, Austria had the option to receive trapped QKD just because to make the bank move.

3. Super-Powerful Computers

PCs, for the most part, encode their data as twofold digit string or bit string. Quantum PCs supercharge the handling power since they utilize quantum bits or qubits which exist in a superposition of states — until they are estimated, qubits can be both "1" and "0" at the same time. Even though the field is as yet being worked on, there remain hints of movement the correct way. D-Wave frameworks uncovered in 2011 their D-Wave One, which has a 128-qubit processor, and afterward, D- Wave Two turned out in the next year and bragged of a 512-qubit processor.
A report from the company says that these are the first commercially available quantum computers in the world. This has remained an issue because it is still unclear if D-Wave's qubits are entangled. Research published in May finds signs of entanglement, but only in a rather small subset of machine qubits. There is confusion as to whether the chips exhibit any real quantum speedup. There has been a recent collaboration between NASA and Google to develop a D-Wave Two Quantum Artificial Intelligence Lab. Scientists at the University of Bristol were able to connect one of their traditional Quantum chips to the Internet so that anyone with a web browser can learn Quantum coding.

4. Improved Microscopes

Some research teams from Japan's Hokkaido University were able to develop the world's first entanglement-enhanced microscope, which made use of differential interference contrast microscopy technique. This particular kind of microscope burns two beams of photons to a material and tests the interference pattern changes depending on whether the beams touch a smooth or irregular surface. Using entangled photons considerably increases the amount of information that the microscope can collect, as measuring one entangled photon provides information about its partner. The Hokkaido was able to build an etched "Q," which was just 17 nanometers above the surface with unparalleled sharpness. Astronomy instruments such as interferometers can have their resolution increased using similar methods. The interferometers are used to search for extrasolar planets, to probe surrounding stars, and to search for space-time ripples or gravitational waves.

5. Biological Compasses

The use of quantum mechanics isn't something used only by humans. It's being observed that birds such as the European Robin use the weird behavior to keep track of their migration. They carry this process out through a light-sensitive protein called cryptochrome, and this may have entangled electrons. As soon as the photons move into the eye, they reach the cryptochrome molecules. Enough energy is provided to break them apart, and this forms two reactive molecules or radicals with the unpaired but still entangled electrons.

The duration the cryptochrome would last is largely dependent on the magnetic field around the bird. The birds have a very sensitive retina, which can easily detect the presence of entangled radicals; this enables the animals to notice a molecular-based magnetic map effectively.

Although, when the entanglement becomes poor, the experiment has shown that the bird will still be able to detect this. Certain kinds of lizards, insects also use this magnetic compass. Crustaceans or insects and mammals. A certain kind of cryptochrome used for magnetic navigation in flies has been detected in the human eyes. There is still debate as to whether it was used by humans for navigation as well.

QUANTUM PHYSICS AS SEEN IN EVERYDAY OBJECTS

At a point, we must feel irritated and slightly confused as to how so many concepts been mentioned here can be applied to our daily lives or used by the different instruments around us. Quantum Physics is one of the highlights of human intellectualism, and its knowledge has helped shape our civilization. Despite this relevance, most people still feel the subject of this field is quite abstruse and cannot be easily grasped by the ordinary mind. In the mind of the public, the concept of quantum physics is seen as a hard concept that is only understood by minds like Einstein and Hawking and another superhuman brain.
The concept of quantum physics is an understanding of the universe, and the universe is all around us, and its operation is based on the

quantum rules. Even though we are so used to the laws of classical physics, and this relates to the universe at a macroscopic level, the understanding of quantum physics still affects various familiar operations. You'll find this list contains various tools and equipment that apply to quantum principle, without we realizing it.

TOASTERS

We are all familiar with the red glow produced by the heating element as we toast our bread. Funny enough, it was the observation if this red light that led physicists to ask questions, questions that birthed the quantum concept. Physicists wanted to know why hot objects shone that particular color of red, a very tough question, and quantum physics came to provide light to it.
Max Planck answered this issue in his theory, where he said that the light been transmitted must be discharged in discrete pieces of vitality, actual products of short, consistent occasions the recurrence of the light. For high-frequency light, the energy quantum is greater than the share of heat energy, which is assigned to that frequency, and this makes it impossible for light to be emitted at such frequency. This prevents the emission of high-frequency light. We could say that the toaster could be a central place where the idea of quantum physics first originated.
Fluorescent Lights
The traditional incandescent light bulb was able to emit light by heating a piece of wire adequately until it gets hot and emit a bright white glow; this is similar to the phenomenon of the toaster. You are enjoying a groundbreaking work of quantum physics whenever you flick on a fluorescent bulb or one of the more recent twisty CFL bulbs; that's quantum physics at work.

In the early 19th century, physicists discovered that all elements found in the periodic table have a unique spectrum. When we heat a vapor of atoms, they will eventually emit light at a small number of discrete wavelengths, and each of the different items will have a different

pattern. The spectral lines were used to classify the composition of new material, and unknown elements such as helium were first discovered through this process.
This is how a fluorescent bulb works: whether the bulb is CFL or long tube, inside the bulb is a tiny bit of mercury vapor that is excited into plasma. Mercury easily emits light at frequencies that fall at the visible spectrum, and eyes will perceive this as white light.

MODERN PHYSICS

This picture, from the Atlas detector at CERN, shows a Higgs boson decaying into two photons. Several recent discoveries, all of which affect how we understand how things work, ranging from the human body to the universe!

The problem of what "stuff " is made of has obsessed philosophers from the beginning. By the 1930s, we had a partial answer, summarized in the table, where we have arranged the five particles which we have talked about up to now in rough order of discovery.

Particle	Date	Mass (MeV)	Charge	B	Strong	EM	Weak	Grav
Electron	1897	0.511	-1	0		X	X	X
Photon	1900	0	0	0		X		X
Proton	1917	938	1	1	X	X	X	X
Neutron	1932`	939	0	1	X	X	X	X
Neutrino	1933	$< 10^{-6}$	0	0			X	X

The column headed "B" shows baryon number: we saw earlier that a neutron could not decay to two photons, and we explained this by introducing a new quantity that counts the number of nucleons present. Note how arbitrary the table seems to be: for example, we know the neutrino has a non-zero mass, but we do not know how big it is. Also, although it describes the particles, it does not explain them in any way.

Earlier on, we wrote down the Dirac equation that does a far better job of describing the electron. Buried in this equation is one of the most remarkable discoveries in physics.

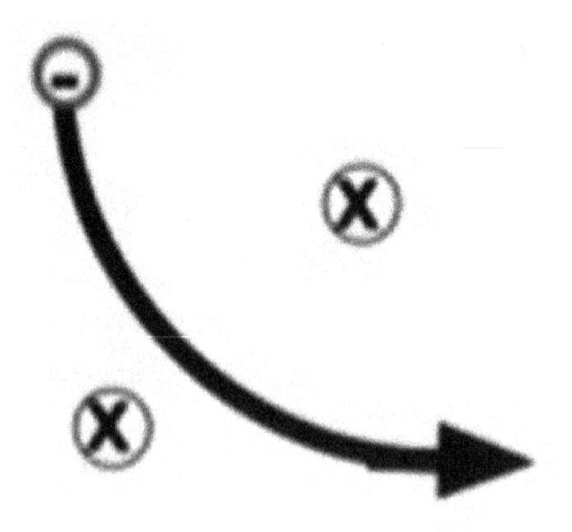

The Dirac equation has a solution for a negatively charged electron in a magnetic field, showing that it curves to the left for a field coming out of the page.

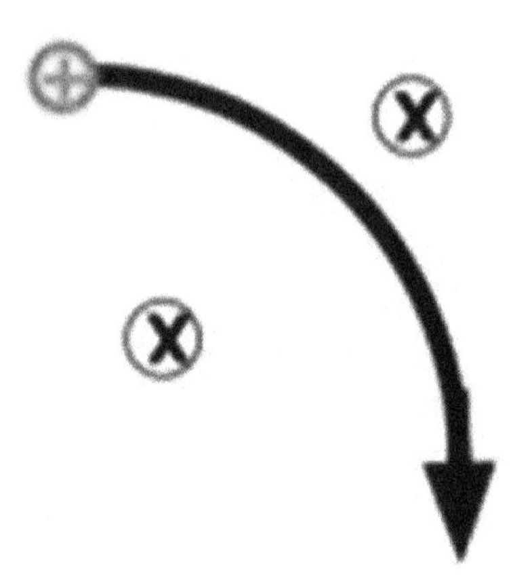

However, it also has a solution for an object identical to the electron except that it is positively charged, so it bends to the right in the same field.

In other words, the Dirac equation predicts anti-matter! As Paul Dirac himself said
"This result is too beautiful to be false; it is more important to have beauty in one's equations than to have them fit experiment."

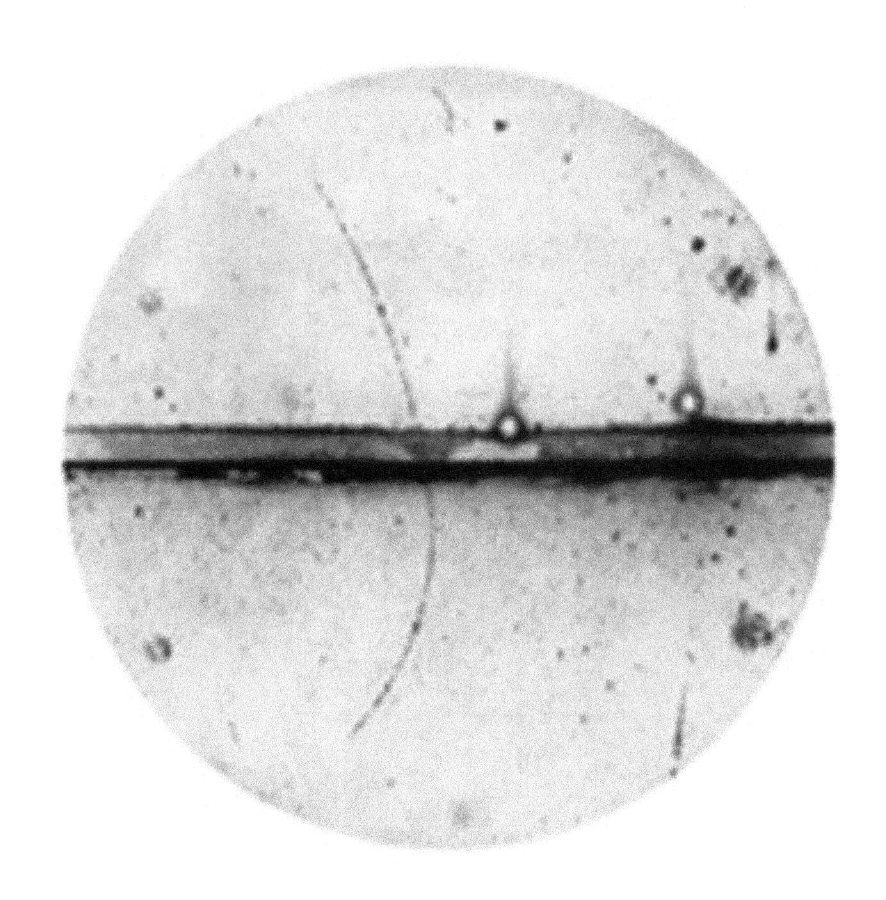

The prediction was confirmed very rapidly, by (in particular) Carl Anderson, who named the particle the positron. In the picture, a positron is coming from the top of the picture, passing through a very thin layer of lead, so it loses energy and then continuing with lower momentum.

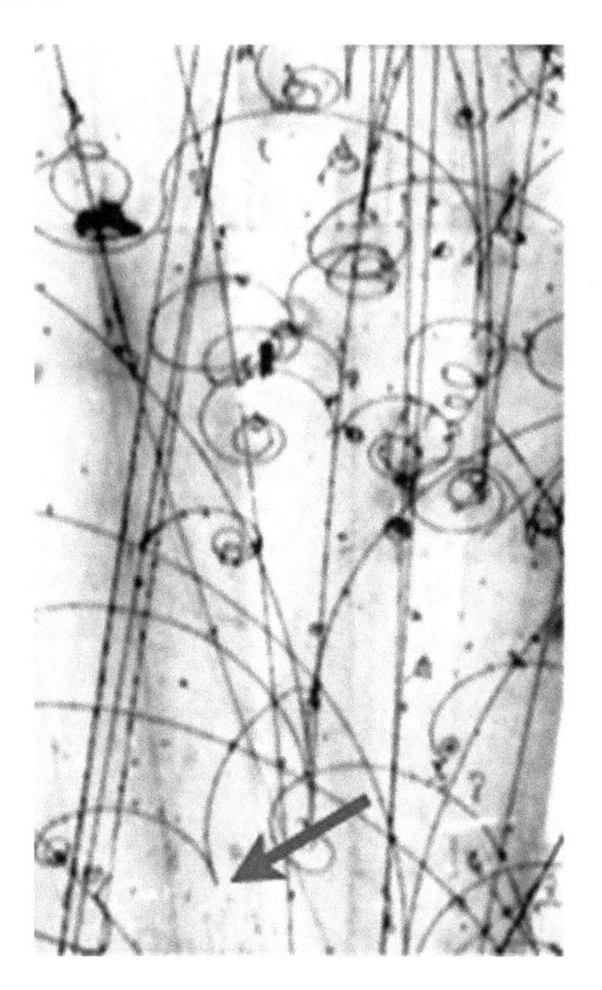

In this picture, you can see many electron-positron pairs created in a hydrogen bubble chamber.

The arrow points to a place where a pair has seemingly appeared out of nothing: the process is $\gamma \rightarrow e^+ + e^-$

Note we are creating matter from energy.
In solid matter, a positron will almost immediately encounter an electron and annihilate $e^+ + e^- \rightarrow \gamma + \gamma$. The photons emerge "back-to-back" with very characteristic energy given by half the total energy of the electron- positron pair, giving 511 keV for each photon.

This is exploited in positron-emission tomography (PET). Some isotopes decay with the emission of a positron (for example, fluorine $^{18}F \rightarrow {}^{18}O + e^+ + \nu$), which immediately annihilates giving photons. These can be analyzed to give the site where the decay happened. In PET scanning, the subject is given a form of glucose with an 18F atom replacing one of the hydrogen atoms in it.

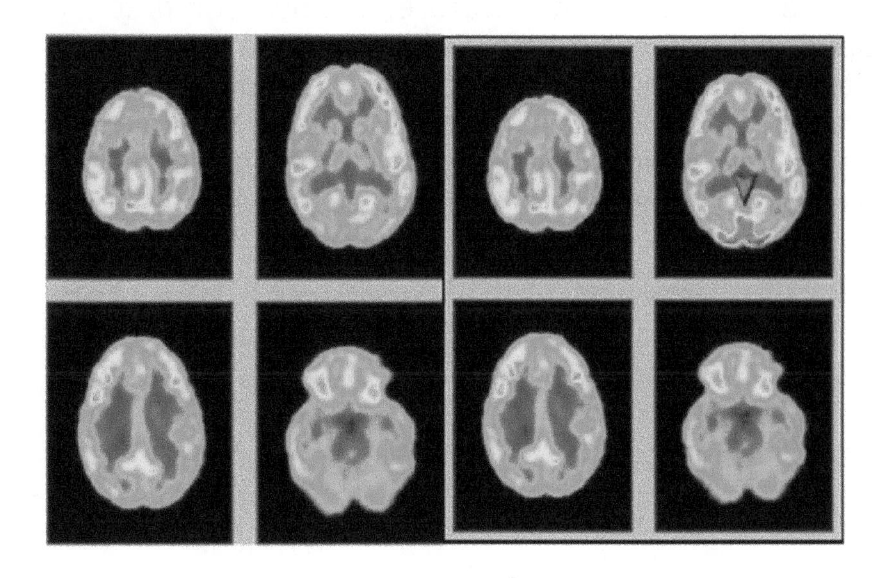

Any cell in the body which is actively using glucose will take this up, so one can create a series of 2-D pictures. Above, you can see on the left a resting brain, on the right one where the brain is being stimulated by color and patterns: the stimulated area is the visual cortex, so you can see someone thinking! Remarkably, the most wide-spread use of anti- matter is to understand the human body, but the radiation dose from the 18F is very low.
The electron is not unique: all particles have anti-particles so that one can create anti-hydrogen, consisting of a positron bound to an anti-

proton. Antimatter has inspired many other ideas. It has been suggested as a fuel for interstellar rocket ships, because when it annihilates, 100% of the mass becomes energy, unlike a nuclear fusion reaction where perhaps 2% could be used. The downside is that it is incredibly expensive to produce and impossible to store with current technology: the best we can do is to store a few dozen atoms in a magnetic field.
In the science fiction literature, the positron first appeared in Isaac Asimov's robot stories ("Caves of Steel," "I, Robot") as the core of the "positronic brain." Wisely, Asimov never attempted to explain how it might work. Most recently, anti-matter as an explosive is the theme behind Dan Brown's "Angels and Demons."

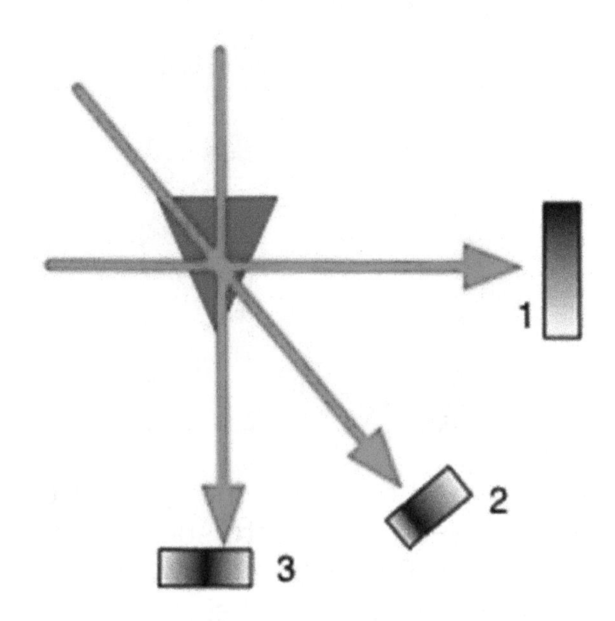

CT SCANNING PRINCIPLES

The medical profession needs to look inside the human body without damaging it. Physicists have provided a wide variety of techniques for doing this, starting with Roentgen's X-rays. A single x-ray picture produces little more than a shadow-gram of the object, so the image of the triangle conveys little information. A series of pictures convey more,

but by combining a large number of images from different angles allows these to be combined into a 3-D picture of the body. This is known as Computed Tomography, or CT, scanning.

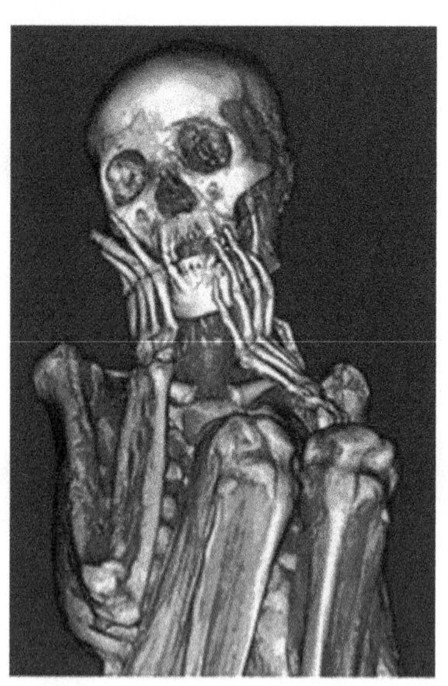

Peruvian mummy

The non-invasive nature of this means that CT scanning can be used for delicate specimens, such as the ominous-looking Peruvian Mummy in the figure. EEG and ECG measure electrical signals from the brain and heart, respectively, and PET scanning and various nuclear tracers allow us to see how metabolic processes work and how strong your bones are. However, the most powerful technique is the MRI scan.

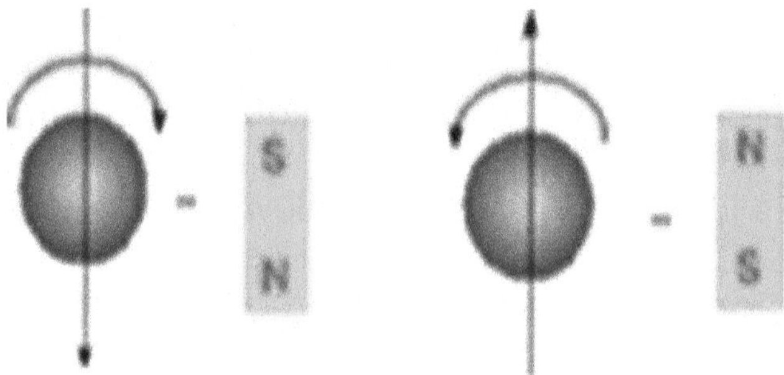

Since protons are charged and spinning, they act like tiny magnets in the same way that electrons do. Rabi first measured the nuclear magnetic moment in 1938. This led to the invention of MRI in 1973. If you place a magnet in a magnetic field, its energy depends on its orientation. Due to quantum mechanics, there are only two possible orientations of spin aligned along the magnetic field (up) or in the opposite direction (down).

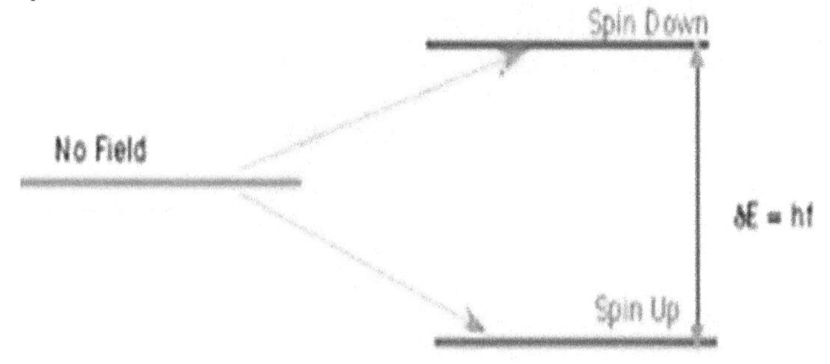

In the absence of the field, there is no magnetic energy, so turning it on gives two possible energy levels, split by a very small amount of energy. A common thing, the distinction between these vitality levels compares to a specific photon vitality/recurrence. On the off chance that the field B = 1Tesla = 10000 Gauss, at that point, the recurrence of the photon is f ≃42.6 MHz, which is in the microwave district.

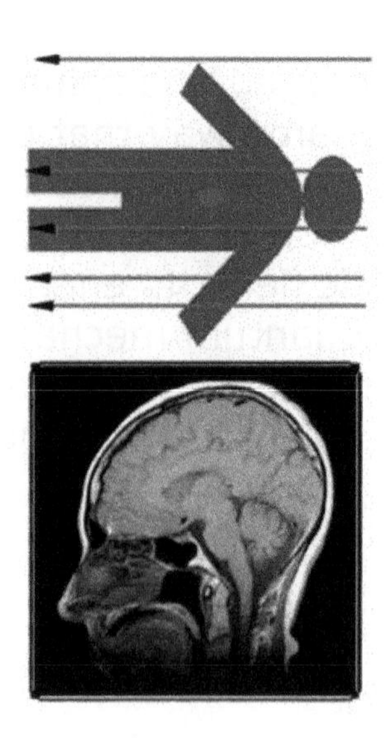

A sign took care of into the issue will be emphatically invested in this specific recurrence if protons are available. Protons are, of course, present as hydrogen nuclei in the form of water and fat molecules, but not in bone. To turn this into an image, we use a varying magnetic field, so the frequency of the emitted photon varies across the object. By scanning across a range of slightly different frequencies, a 2-D image can be built up, and this can then be assembled into a 3-D picture

In the diagram, you can see a "slice" through the head. Note skull bone appears as white as it contains no water. MRI picks out the difference between fat and blood-vessels because of very slightly varying frequencies to produce a beautifully detailed picture. This is the only method for the detection of many tumors, as well as showing "soft- tissue" damage that X-rays do not do well.

It is amusing that the technique was originally known as Nuclear Magnetic Resonance Imaging, but was changed to MRI to avoid the negative connotations of nuclear physics!

Problem 1: PET (positron-Emission topography) uses
- X-rays
- Anti-matter
- The magnetic fields of protons
- Electrical signals from the brain
- Electrical signals from the brain

Problem 2: CT Scanning uses
- X-rays
- Anti-matter
- The magnetic fields of protons
- Electrical signals from the brain
- Electrical signals from the brain

Problem 3: MRI (Magnetic resonance imaging) uses
- X-rays
- Anti-matter
- The magnetic fields of protons
- Electrical signals from the brain
- Electrical signals from the brain
- Elementary Particles and the Higgs Boson

IS BASIC RESEARCH WORTHWHILE?

The effort to discover the Higgs boson is probably the largest scientific research effort in history. We have touched on a few others, such as SNO. The cost is huge: although discovering the Higgs was not the sole aim of CERN, the total cost of the LHC is B$5 to B$8. This is not very precise accounting: however, it depends very much on what is included in the cost. How can we justify doing fundamental research when it has such a staggering associated cost and no obvious payback?

However, it is important to keep in mind not just how powerful undirected research can be, but how it can affect unrelated areas. To give one example, Rabi was certainly not trying to understand the human body when he discovered the magnetic moment of the proton. Still, MRI, which builds on his discovery, provides a unique way of imaging the body and is a billion-dollar industry today. In 1988, Tim Berners-Lee was a CERN employee when he invented the World Wide Web as a way for physicists separated geographically to collaborate. Since CERN is an international organization, it has a policy of not copyrighting or patenting any inventions. The fortunes of all internet companies depend on Google alone is currently worth about B$340. In 2011 it had indexed

1 trillion pages, and a mere .001 ¢/page license would pay the annual budget of CERN!

In conclusion, Atlas and CMS give us the best check of our theories ever. Good science costs money and requires commitment. We do not know what it's going to produce (that's research!), and the spinoffs may take 50 years to arrive.

Problem Solutions

1. PET (Positron-Emission Topography) uses anti-matter in the form of positrons.
2. CT Scanning uses X-rays
3. MRI (Magnetic Resonance Imaging) uses the magnetic fields of protons

CONCLUSION

Maybe, indeed certainly, I will repeat myself a little bit, but, as you know by now, this is one of my "strategies" of divulgation, which many people appreciate and, therefore, I keep doing it.
First of all, let me make one observation that is certainly not new to you. Quantum Mechanics (QM) was born in the same years as the theory of relativity and was, in a similar way, a reference theory for the whole 20th century. However, it has never really been able to get out of the narrow circle of insiders. One might think that this is due to the mathematical difficulties of the expressions that govern the wave function and not only complex plane and similar things. No, it is not enough to explain its "ghettoization."

There must be something different that appears to block its revelation. Relativity is no not as much as that, yet it has entered overwhelmingly into everyday language. Besides, QM is at the premise of the apparent multitude of mechanical developments of today, from nuclear vitality to PC microelectronics, from advanced tickers to lasers, semiconductor frameworks, photoelectric cells, indicative and treatment hardware for some illnesses. To put it, today, we can "live" in a "cutting edge" way, on account of QM and its applications.

Our mind, as I mentioned earlier, seems to be based on quantum processes, including state overlaps, the wave collapses, and entanglement situations. The real difficulty lies in its "counterintuitive" postulates about the reality of nature. A real discomfort in entering an unknown and absurd world like Alice's one. Let's not feel too inferior, though. The founding fathers themselves lived this situation to the limit of the absurd. Could one believe that nature followed completely arbitrary rules or, instead, was it all an appearance due to the lack of information, of a deterministic kind, still missing?
The very creator of the very general and ultra-confirmed principle of indeterminacy (Heisenberg), said: "I remember the long discussions with Bohr, which made us stay up late at night and left us in a state of deep depression, not to say real despair. I kept walking alone in the park, and I kept thinking that it was impossible that nature was as absurd as it appeared to us from the experiments." In a nutshell, there is no defined and describable reality, but an objectively indistinct reality, composed of superimposed states.
Let's pick up on two essential points that we have learned to know, but certainly not to understand:

1. Every action of the finer structure of matter is characterized only and only by its probability of happening. Phenomena completely causal, not deterministic. But, above all, by the indistinct separation between the observed object, the measuring instrument, and the observer.

2. It is possible that, under certain conditions, what happens in a certain place can drastically influence what happens in a completely different place, instantly. This leads to the phenomenon of entanglement, the twisting of particles that have had an interaction in their past (but recent research also seems to admit "contacts" in the future) or that were born "together." Although completely separate, they always represent the same entity. An action performed on one has an instantaneous effect on the other.
Perhaps you've already noticed the real problem with the QM. On the one hand, the difficulty of dealing with concepts that are too far removed from everyday reality, and on the other hand, the difficulty of using proper language to explain this absurd world. Math can also describe it, but the letters and words of this strange alphabet are missing.

Exceptional, in this respect, was Feynman's work with his diagrams applied to QED (which we now know quite well).

It is intriguing to cite a sentence by Max Born about this: " definitive inception of the trouble lies in the reality (or philosophical rule) that we are constrained to utilize the expressions of basic language when we wish to portray a marvel, not by legitimate or numerical examination, yet by an image speaking to the creative mind. Everyday language has developed by everyday experience and can never outperform these cutoff points. Traditional material science has confined itself to the utilization of ideas of this sort; by examining noticeable movements, it has created two different ways of speaking to them by basic cycles: moving particles and waves. There is no other method of giving a pictorial portrayal of movements - we need to apply it even in the area of nuclear cycles, where old-style material science separates."
More or less, the depiction of the QM itself could be intensely affected by our "work of art" graphic cutoff points.
Often, therefore, the founding fathers themselves have used analogies and similarities to express purely mathematical concepts. They, however, must be considered for what they are and should not be given any real and concrete validity. This is a huge problem for our brain (especially today) even if — perhaps — it would have all the basics to use an adequate language, but still too indistinct to be formulated correctly: Feynman's diagrams, I repeat, are a wonderful attempt in that direction.
Niels Bohr himself used graphic analogies to try to support such absurd theories for our classical language. Famous is the white vase representing, at the same time, two black social profiles.

A state of superimposition between two realities existing instantly (two states or — maybe two Universes?). This type of analogy has influenced many optical illusion games and even artistic currents (think of Picasso).
It is a pity that these interpretative efforts, combined with Feynman's more complete and refined efforts, do not find their way into schools to adequately prepare young people to "stammer" their first quantum words and to begin a primitive language that would allow them, today, to understand, at least partially, the reality of Alice. And not only passively undergo the most wonderful technological applications that are now an integral part of their physical body. Real "appendages," which, however, act unconsciously, independently of any mental command. Unconditional reflexes and nothing more.
After all, de Broglie advanced his daring hypothesis precisely by following the symmetries of visible Nature. He only associated with the matter in general, what happened to the light. In short: if light manifests itself under a double aspect, undulating and corpuscular, why not think that also matter follows the same rule? It is enough to associate to each corpuscle of matter a wave of a certain length, that is, a phenomenon extended to the space surrounding the particle. The dualistic nature (particle-waves) applies to all particles, such as electrons, atoms, and other moving entities.
However, the basic problem remains open (still today the subject of discussion and interpretation), which we have mentioned. The wave of matter that commands the particle can be deterministic, and therefore still unknown in its real structure (in line with Einstein's idea) or, instead, a different representation of the same particle and therefore follow the rules of complete a causality (Copenhagen school).

In one way or another, however, it must be concluded that the light or a beam of electrons is nothing but a "train" of electromagnetic waves, but also a jet of "bullets" as in the double-slit experiment.
While remaining in this basic ambiguity, Schrödinger formulated the equation that perfectly describes every adulatory property of matter through its wave function. It allows us to describe every single behavior and, above all, to calculate the probability distribution to find a particle inside the associated wave.
Overwhelming mathematics that, however, does not annul the fact that Schrödinger himself did not believe in the actual concreteness of this representation. Everything and the opposite of everything (conceptually), but described in the same way.
However, its equation confirms what Feynman's experiment illustrated above: a particle can occupy ALL possible positions within the associated wave. By occupying all possible positions, it no longer has an actual place of existence or direction. It automatically cancels any possible prediction of its future except in purely probabilistic terms (the QED is increasingly understandable... don't you think?). The pilot wave or a hidden variable does not change the action of Nature and its probabilistic description.
Once again, we fall back on Heisenberg's principle. In classical mechanics, deterministic essence automatically allows you to predict the future if you have exact information about the position and speed of a particle. Let us remember, in this regard, that the first mathematical methods that allowed the calculation of an orbit of a "planetary" particle were based (and still are based) on the knowledge of at least three positions and three velocities, such as to allow the solution of an orbit characterized by six unknowns. Too easy for microscopic particles.

The probabilistic conception leads inexorably to the principle of indeterminacy, inherent in the whole microcosm: either one knows the position or one knows the speed. To know both with accuracy is impossible. Otherwise, the particle would be located, and the wave would collapse. And we go back to the starting point again. Whether there is an initial causality (completely unknown) or not at all. In a nutshell, the double-slit experiment perfectly illustrates all the problems of QM.
It's worth reflecting on Einstein's dramatic emotional situation. While he was giving physical reality a perfectly deterministic representation, he found himself involved in a representation that led to the complete a causality of nature. He said:" Quantum radiation theories interest me very much, but I wouldn't want to be forced to abandon narrow causality without trying to defend it to the limit.

Yet, no physicist has contributed as much as Einstein to the creation of Quantum Physics. What he demonstrated about it (and for it) was enough and advanced for a scientific career of the highest level (not for nothing earned him the Nobel Prize). It is, therefore, easy to understand his existential drama, which never left him until his death. A mixture of anger, wounded pride, unshakable confidence, and despair at not being able to demonstrate his certainties.

CPSIA information can be obtained
at www.ICGtesting.com
Printed in the USA
BVHW051547090321
602118BV00003B/165

This mix of frustration, exaltation, hope, disappointment, innovation, and conservatism has permeated all the great minds that gave birth to QM. A very choral work and certainly not a puzzle of individual ideas. Each one, almost unwillingly (sometimes even against their purposes), did nothing but put an extra brick to a building that was becoming an incredible skyscraper with an increasingly solid, unassailable foundation.
Perhaps this very unique way in the history of science to formulate a more and more complete and refined theory, by many higher minds, could make people understand that QM is something inherent in the human mind, but that it has extreme difficulty in coming out of the closet. Surely, the knowledge of the language of Classical Physics has made giant steps forward, but not so far from the almost unconscious insights of Democritus and Epicurus. In a nutshell, the mind must be trained to indulge in a reality that is only historically and culturally absurd.
The more we get into the very essence of QM and its principles, the more fundamental and complete the double-slit experiment becomes. A proper scientific masterpiece, a manifesto itself of the future of the human intellect.

QM not only as Science but as a school of life.